WIGS AT WORK

Sir Alan Herbert was born in 1890, and was educated at Winchester, and New College, Oxford, where he learned his first law and took a First Class in the Honours School of Jurisprudence. He served with the Royal Naval Division in Gallipoli and France, 1914–17. He married Gwendolen Quilter (in bellbottom trousers) on 31 December 1914: they have four children and fourteen grandchildren. He was called to the Bar in 1918 and was, for two years, private secretary to Sir Leslie Scott, K.C., M.P. From 1935 to 1950 he was a Member of Parliament (Independent) for Oxford University. In the last war he served with the River Emergency Service, Thames, London, and as a Petty Officer in the Naval Auxiliary Patrol. He has been working for *Punch* since 1910. His books include *The Secret Battle*, *Independent Member*, *Number Nine*, *Why Waterloo?*, *Uncommon Law*, *Holy Deadlock*, *The Water Gipsies* (available as a Penguin), *Made for Man*, and many volumes of light verse. He was also the author of the libretto of *La Vie Parisienne*, *Tantivy Towers*, *Derby Day*, *Helen*, *Mother of Pearl*, *Big Ben*, *Bless the Bride*, *Tough at the Top*, and other musical productions, in eight of which he worked with Sir Charles Cochran.

A. P. HERBERT

WIGS AT WORK

PENGUIN BOOKS

Penguin Books Ltd, Harmondsworth, Middlesex, England
Penguin Books Australia Ltd, Ringwood, Victoria, Australia

—

Published in Penguin Books 1966
This Collection copyright © A. P. Herbert, 1966

—

Made and printed in Great Britain
by Cox & Wyman Ltd., London, Fakenham and Reading
Set in Monotype Imprint

Contents

CONTENTS

Preamble

THE venerable Haddock is proud to join the fine company of Penguins. In the last forty years I must have written something like 150 Misleading Cases. Here is a small selection of 34. Some go back a long way, but the last three are concerned with computers, the Common Market (Britain already a member) and 'radio pirates', so Haddock cannot be very far behind the times.

Mr Bumble's famous saying on the law is nearly always quoted as a general condemnation. In fact, it was applied to a particular point on which he had particular information:

'You were present,' said Mr Brownlow, 'and indeed are the more guilty of the two, in the eye of the law; for the law supposes that your wife acts under your direction.'

'If the law supposes that,' said Mr Bumble, 'the law is a ass – a idiot. If that's the eye of the law, the law is a bachelor; and the worst I wish the law is, that his eye may be opened by experience.'

If I had ever thought that our law was generally an ass I should not have been called to the Bar nearly fifty years ago, nor should I have given so much time and toil to the sincerest form of flattery. I have in fact a warm admiration for those who wear the wig, for their lucid language, delicate reasoning and – don't laugh – their pride in the pursuit of justice and order. 'Lucid?' you may say with surprise. Certainly, when they are roaming free the plains of the Common Law where so many splendid crops of principle and practice were sown by former gentlemen in wigs. They tend and improve them still, making new law, now and then, if you will, grafting and pruning, but the fruit is well bred and the process clear. Here and there an ancient plant should be dug up and allowed to die, the distinction between felony and misdemeanour, for example, and, some think, between libel and slander: but it is too deeply rooted in history for the judges to touch. Then you must blame not 'the law' but Parliament which has failed to use a spade.

Again, when you hear the gentlemen in wigs talking, it seems, Double Dutch, and reeling round in conflicting circles, put it down to Parliament, not the fraternity of the law. They are struggling, stifled, in a labyrinth of modern legislation, constructed brilliantly by Parliamentary draftsmen, who are not allowed to explain what they meant, even if they know.

But we must be charitable, even to the authors of the wordy, woolly statutes we all detest. In my fifteen years in the House of Commons I devised (but was not always allowed to present) about fifteen Bills. I drafted many of them myself, determined to show that it was possible to make good law in simple intelligible English. Nearly always I had to hand them over to the professionals – and then what a change! When my simple Bills came out of that oven I could hardly understand their sense or purpose. My simple clauses had left inviting loopholes for the ingenious citizen or counsel which must be barred with provisos and 'savings'. I had forgotten that other statutes had dealt with the same subject, and these must be repealed, or modified with 'notwithstandings'. 'Legislation by reference' sullied the virgin page:

(iii) Subsection (2) of Section 26, Subsection (i) of Section 27, and Section 31 of the Supreme Court of Judicature (Consolidation) Act 1925, shall be construed and have effect subject to the provisions of this Act.

Or:

The expression 'water' has the meaning attributed to it in Section 17 (subsection 3) of the Land Drainage Act 1930.

Moses had no such trouble: 'Thou shalt not commit adultery' is fine and simple. But I wonder how many clauses and pages there would be in a consolidating Act setting out the whole of our law upon that one injunction. In Latey's Divorce there are three fat pages devoted to 'Definition' alone. It is not a simple thing to be simple.

The law is not always a ass, but it is often a enigma. So I hope that, whatever you may think of the laws, made in Westminster or tinkered by the Temple, you will find nothing in these pages to make you think less of 'the law', meaning the gentlemen in wigs. If I laugh at some of them, I laugh with affection and respect.

Here and there, in a modest note, I have been able to mutter 'I told you so.' More often, as the old song says, 'They wouldn't believe me.' But I find comfort in the following verses which all failed and failing reformers should keep upon their desks:

THE CONTENTED MIND

It gives me shy but sharp delight
To think how often I am right;

How often, and, alas, how long
The world insists on being wrong.

In pub and press the fools dissent
From what I find self-evident,

And end the maddening debate
Reluctantly – perhaps too late.

It can be comforting, I know,
To say at last 'I told you so',

But in the public interest
A quick decision would be best:

For while they dicker and delay
The mischief's done – and it will stay.

How different the world would be
If all, *at once*, agreed with me!

But still it gives me shy delight
To recollect that I was right.

For further studies see *Uncommon Law, Codd's Last Case*, and *Bardot M.P.*, all published by Methuen.

A.P.H.

'Who Giveth this Woman?'

REGINA *v.* HADDOCK

MR ALBERT HADDOCK gave evidence today in the appeal from his conviction by the justices of Rivertown, under the Act of 1860, for brawling in church.

Sir Anthony Slatt, Q.C. (cross-examining) : Then, I believe, the Vicar said: 'Who giveth this Woman to be married to this Man?' What happened next?

Haddock: I said 'As a matter of fact, *I* do.'

Sir Anthony: Loudly?

Haddock: I believe in speaking up, sir.

Mr Justice Plush: Quite right. What should he have said, Sir Anthony?

Sir Anthony: My lord, no words are prescribed. The question 'Who giveth . . .?' is followed immediately by these directions: 'Then shall they give their troth to each other in this manner. The Minister, receiving the Woman *at her father's or friend's hands.* shall cause the Man with his right hand to take the Woman by her right hand,' and so on. My lord, in my submission, it is not intended that the 'father or friend' shall use any words: and, in fact, as a rule, he is content to make a formal gesture and quietly stand aside.

The Judge: But how, then, is anyone to know who he is?

Sir Anthony: My lord, it is assumed that the person making the gesture . . .

The Judge: 'Assumed'? But he may be an impostor – some violent bully who by duress or drugs is forcing an unwilling woman into a union which is repugnant. I think Mr Haddock was quite right to make himself, and his consent, manifest. Did he 'announce his identity' as the telephone book says?

Sir Anthony: Yes, my lord. But that, my lord, was not all the accused said.

The Judge: Oh? What else did you say, Mr Haddock?

The Witness: 'I am Albert Haddock,' I said, my lord, 'the

father of this beautiful girl: and I am very glad of this opportunity to say a few words. I may say it's the first chance I've had to say a few words, without insult or interruption, for about six months. It is a singular fact, worthy of study by the anthropologists, that a month or two before his daughter's marriage, the father, the husband, the bread-winner, who has made the whole affair possible, is afflicted with imbecility – that is, in the estimation of the female members of the tribe. They fuss and buzz about like a swarm of bees, arranging, planning, arguing, advising, whispering in corners, yelling over the telephone, buying this and ordering that. The only person never consulted, never allowed to open his mouth, is Daddy, who "doesn't understand". Daddy is only fit for footing the bills. Yes, Vicar, I do give this Woman away, but I'm also giving the wedding-dress, and three, at least, of those horrible bridesmaids' dresses. I can't stand yellow – they all know that. "Pale blue," I said, "anything but *yellow*," I said. But oh, no – "Daddy doesn't understand" – and there they are, poor girls, like a clutch of canaries. What's more, I'm giving the party afterwards. I'd like to discuss that. I never know why it's the *bride's* father who has to cough up for the reception. I speak feelingly, Vicar, because, as you know, I've seven daughters. Doris is the fourth to get married, and there are still three to go. Next time – and I give you all fair notice – there'll have to be some other arrangement. Fair do's.'

The Judge : I have five daughters myself, Mr Haddock. I know what you mean.

The Witness : Thank you, my lord. Well, 'Don't think I begrudge the money,' I said, 'it isn't that. But if I have to cough up every time, I might at least be allowed to have my way about the bridesmaids' dresses. *And* about the wine. I don't like champagne – hardly anybody does, if the truth were told. Horrible drink. "Let's be different," I said, "let's have a nice still Hock – or some of that Alsatian. Much better for everybody – and nobody who matters will miss those ridiculous bubbles." But oh, no – it's "Daddy doesn't understand."'

The Judge : The Court is with you. But, Mr Haddock, I am not quite clear. Did you actually say all this?

The Witness : Yes, my lord – or something like it.

The Judge : Excellent. Go on.

The Witness : 'And *then,*' I said, my lord, 'the extraordinary thing is this! On the day of the race – I mean the match – at the last minute, when the poor bride is hysterical and as likely as not to throw herself out of the window – *all* the women who have been bossing the show for six months go off to the church and leave her alone in the house. *And who with?* Why, with the incapable *man* – the half-witted Father! I can tell you, it was a job to get poor Doris to the starting-gate at all. I had to use the *sal volatile*, and that's a drill I'm not familiar with. How I suffered!'

The Judge : How it all comes back! Go on.

The Witness : It was about then, my lord, that I noticed the Vicar whispering to the verger, who made a stately exit. 'However,' I said, 'thanks to me, we made it.'

The Judge : You made what?

The Witness : The starting-gate, my lord. But just as we were coming round the turn into the nave – all in step with the music, and going well – we'd rehearsed it several times, my lord – some lunatic female dashes out of her pew and hisses 'You're on the wrong side – you're on the wrong side.' 'I'm not,' I said. 'Go away.' 'I ought to know,' she said, 'I've done this five times.' Then she disappeared. Well, she was wrong, of course, my lord, but it shook me – put us out of step. We get to the top, and I stand there looking like a riderless horse – that's all right – but when we get to my little bit, there's nothing for me to say. Suddenly I thought, 'If I've got to go through all this three more times, there must be better arrangements.'

The Judge : You mentioned this in your address? It was in the nature of a dignified protest?

The Witness : Yes, my lord. 'I'm not being obstructive,' I said, 'I said I'd give Doris away, and so I will, though after all this many a man would change his mind, and where would you all be then?'

The Judge : Mr Attorney, where would they all have been then?

Sir Anthony : Milord, without further instructions, I should not like to say.

The Judge : Very well. And that was all?

The Witness : Yes, my lord. No, my lord, there was one more thing. I'm glad you reminded me. I said a word about the *time* of these ghastly affairs. *Months* ago, my lord, I said, ' *Don't* have it at two o'clock!' But, of course, Daddy didn't understand, and two o'clock was precisely the time the frantic women chose.

The Judge : Why do you object to that?

The Witness : Well, my lord, just because two young folk want to get married, I don't see why all their friends should be expected to miss a whole day's work and put on tails and toppers at twelve noon. The last lawful hour for weddings used to be 3.0, but many years ago Parliament very wisely passed a new law permitting them up till 6.0. Well, 5.30 would do very well – that's what we did with June and Joyce. By the time the cake-cutting and all that is over it's a reasonable hour for a drink – even champagne. Three o'clock in the afternoon is a disgusting hour for drinking – especially champagne.

The Judge : I think you're so right.

The Witness : My lord, when the other two were done, we had a nice stand-up supper, with a band and dancing. The bridal pair took the first dance alone – a very pretty picture; and June, I remember, even danced with her contemptible Papa. About 9.30 or 10.0 they tootled off to the Savoy, or somewhere, leaving us all happy; and the next day they went abroad. That's the thing. Now, with a two o'clock affair the wretched guests are left high and dry in their ridiculous clothes at half-past four in the afternoon – dressed up for a Midsummer Night's Dream with Titania and Oberon gone. There's nothing to do but have another drink, and after champagne any other drink is lethal. All because the couple insist on rushing off to some foreign country this afternoon. 'Heaven knows,' I said, 'where these two are going – nobody tells Papa, of *course* – but if they're going to Sicily, why couldn't they go to Sicily to-morrow? After all, they've caused all this costly fuss – they're going to spend their whole lives together, and it wouldn't be a bad thing if they started it by showing some consideration for others. I call it rather selfish.' And about then, my lord, Constable Boot stole up the nave and took me away.

The Judge: In my opinion this prosecution should never have been brought. There is, as the Attorney-General has pointed out, this undoubted and surprising hiatus in the marriage service. Everywhere else all concerned are told precisely what to say and do – 'The Man shall answer "I will"' and so on. Here a question is prescribed but no answer is provided. The question, presumably, has some importance, or it would not be put at all. Some answer therefore must be intended. Mr Haddock was expected to say something: but what he should say was left to his discretion. It may well be, as he has suggested, that originally this moment was designed as an occasion for the bride's father to deliver a patriarchal address, giving to old and young the benefit of his experience and wisdom. One witness thought that the whole business of 'giving away' was a barbarous relic of the father's proprietary interest in his young – the head of the tribe 'giving' his daughter in exchange for twenty fat oxen, and so on. I prefer, myself, to think that it is a wholesome safeguard against the malefactor, strengthening the evidence of true consent. But there the question is, and I have only to decide whether what Mr Haddock said in answer to it was 'riotous, violent, or indecent'. I think, on the contrary, that what he said, though perhaps insensitive and tactless here and there, was in substance sound and sensible. Certainly, I can find no evidence of anything that amounts to brawling. The Attorney-General, I know, is fussed about 'creating a precedent'. The Church, he says, is afraid that if Mr Haddock is discharged all the fathers will do as he did. I have no fear of that: few fathers have the fortitude of Mr Haddock. Besides, if necessary, the service can be amended. The prosecution is dismissed. All possible costs to be paid by the Crown.

20 July 1955

Note: A kind and learned friend tells me that this appeal should have come before the Quarter Sessions. Very well. But I prefer Mr Justice Plush.

The Reasonable Man

FARDELL *v.* POTTS

THE Court of Appeal today delivered judgment in this important case.

The Master of the Rolls: In this case the appellant was a Mrs Fardell, a woman, who, while navigating a motor-launch on the River Thames, collided with the respondent, who was navigating a punt, as a result of which the respondent was immersed and caught cold. The respondent brought an action for damages, in which it was alleged that the collision and subsequent immersion were caused by the negligent navigation of the appellant. In the Court below the learned judge decided that there was evidence on which the jury might find that the defendant had not taken reasonable care, and, being of that opinion, very properly left to the jury the question whether in fact she had failed to use reasonable care or not. The jury found for the plaintiff and awarded him two hundred and fifty pounds damages. This verdict we are asked to set aside on the ground of misdirection by the learned judge, the contention being that the case should never have been allowed to go to the jury; and this contention is supported by a somewhat novel proposition, which has been ably, though tediously, argued by Sir Ethelred Rutt.

The Common Law of England has been laboriously built about a mythical figure – the figure of 'The Reasonable Man'. In the field of jurisprudence this legendary individual occupies the place which in another science is held by the Economic Man, and in social and political discussions by the Average or Plain Man. He is an ideal, a standard, the embodiment of all those qualities which we demand of the good citizen. No matter what may be the particular department of human life which falls to be considered in these Courts, sooner or later we have to face the question: Was this or was it not the conduct of a reasonable man? Did the defendant take such care to avoid shooting the plaintiff in the stomach as might reasonably be expected of a reasonable man? (*Moocat* v. *Radley* (1883) 2 Q.B.) Did the plaintiff take such precautions to inform himself of the circumstances as any reasonable man would expect of an ordinary person having the ordinary knowledge of an ordinary person of the habits of wild bulls when goaded with garden-forks and the persistent agitation of red flags? (*Williams* v. *Dogbody* (1841) 2 A.C.)

I need not multiply examples. It is impossible to travel anywhere or to travel for long in that confusing forest of learned judgments which constitutes the Common Law of England without encountering the Reasonable Man. He is at every turn, an ever-present help in time of trouble, and his apparitions mark the road to equity and right. There has never been a problem, however difficult, which His Majesty's judges have not in the end been able to resolve by asking themselves the simple question, 'Was this or was it not the conduct of a reasonable man?' and leaving that question to be answered by the jury.

This noble creature stands in singular contrast to his kinsman the Economic Man, whose every action is prompted by the single spur of selfish advantage and directed to the single end of monetary gain. The Reasonable Man is always thinking of others; prudence is his guide, and 'Safety First', if I may borrow a contemporary catchword, is his rule of life. All solid virtues are his, save only that peculiar quality by which the affection of other men is won. For it will not be pretended that socially he is much less objectionable than the Economic Man. Though any given example of his behaviour must command our admiration, when taken in the mass his acts create a very different set of impressions. He is one who invariably looks where he is going, and is careful to examine the immediate foreground before he executes a leap or bound; who neither star-gazes nor is lost in meditation when approaching trap-doors or the margin of a dock; who records in every case upon the counterfoils of cheques such ample details as are desirable, scrupulously substitutes the word 'Order' for the word 'Bearer', crosses the instrument 'a/c Payee only', and registers the package in which it is dispatched; who never mounts a moving omnibus, and does not alight from any car while the train is in motion; who investigates exhaustively the *bona fides* of every mendicant before distributing alms, and will inform himself of the history and habits of a dog before administering a caress; who believes no gossip, nor repeats it, without firm basis for believing it to be true; who never drives his ball till those in front of him have definitely vacated the putting-green which is his own objective; who never from one year's end to another makes an excessive demand upon his wife, his neighbours, his servants, his ox, or his ass; who in the way of business looks only for that narrow margin of profit which twelve men such as himself would reckon to be 'fair', and contemplates his fellow-merchants, their agents, and their goods, with that degree of suspicion and distrust which the law deems admirable; who never swears, gambles, or loses his temper; who uses nothing except in moderation, and even while he flogs his child is meditating only on the golden mean. Devoid, in short, of any human weakness, with not one single saving vice, *sans* prejudice, procrastination, ill-nature, avarice, and absence of mind, as careful for his own safety as he is for that of others, this excellent but odious character stands like a monument in our Courts of Justice, vainly appealing to his fellow-citizens to order their lives after his own example.

I have called him a myth; and, in so far as there are few, if any, of his mind and temperament to be found in the ranks of living men, the title is well chosen. But it is a myth which rests upon solid and even, it may be, upon permanent foundations. The Reasonable Man is fed and kept alive by the most valued and enduring of our juridical institutions – the common jury. Hateful as he must necessarily be to any ordinary citizen who privately considers him, it is a curious paradox that where two or three are gathered together in one place they will with one accord pretend an admiration for him; and, when they are gathered together in the formidable surroundings of a British jury, they are easily persuaded that they themselves are, each and generally, reasonable men. Without stopping to consider how strange a chance it must have been that has picked fortuitously from a whole people no fewer than twelve examples of a species so rare, they immediately invest themselves with the attributes of the Reasonable Man, and are therefore at one with the Courts in their anxiety to support the tradition that such a being in fact exists. Thus it is that while the Economic Man has under the stress of modern conditions almost wholly disappeared from view his Reasonable cousin has gained in power with every case in which he has figured.

To return, however, as every judge must ultimately return, to the case which is before us – it has been urged for the appellant, and my own researches incline me to agree, that in all that mass of authorities which bears upon this branch of the law *there is no single mention of a Reasonable Woman.* It was ably insisted before us that such an omission, extending over a century and more of judicial pronouncements, must be something more than a coincidence; that among the innumerable tributes to the Reasonable Man there might be expected at least some passing reference to a reasonable person of the opposite sex; that no such reference is found, for the simple reason that no such being is contemplated by the law; that legally at least there *is* no Reasonable Woman, and that therefore in this case the learned judge should have directed the jury that, while there was evidence on which they might find that the defendant had not come up to the standard required of a Reasonable Man, her conduct was only what was to be expected of a woman, as such.

It must be conceded at once that there is merit in this contention, however unpalatable it may at first appear. The appellant relies largely on *Baxter's Case,* 1639 (2 Bole, at page 100), in which it was held that for the purposes of estover the wife of a tenant by the mesne was at law in the same position as an ox or other cattle *demenant* (to which a modern parallel may perhaps be found in the statutory regulations of many railway companies, whereby, for the purposes of freight, a typewriter is counted as a musical instrument). It is probably no mere chance that in our legal textbooks the problems relating to married women are usually considered immediately after the pages devoted to idiots and lunatics. Indeed, there is respectable authority for saying that at Common Law this was the status of a woman. Recent legislation has whittled away a great part of this venerable conception, but so far as concerns the law of negligence, which is our present consideration, I am persuaded that it remains intact. It is no bad thing that the law of the land should here and there conform with the known facts of every-day experience. The view that there exists a class of beings, illogical, impulsive, careless, irresponsible, extravagant, preju-diced, and vain, free for the most part from those worthy and repellent excellences which distinguish the Reasonable Man, and devoted to the irrational arts of pleasure and attraction, is one which should be as welcome and as well accepted in our Courts as it is in our drawing-rooms – and even in Parliament. The odd stipulation is often heard there that some new Com-mittee or Council shall consist of so many persons 'one of which must be a woman': the assumption being that upon scientific principles of selection no woman would be added to a body having serious deliberative functions. That assumption, which is at once accepted and resented by those who maintain the complete equality of the sexes, is not founded, as they suppose, in some prejudice of Man but in the considered judgments of Nature. I find that at Common Law a Reasonable Woman does not exist. The contention of the respondent fails and the appeal must be allowed. Costs to be costs in the action, above and below, but not costs in the case.

Bungay, L. J., and Blow, L. J., concurred.

9 July 1924

Slander at Sea

TEMPER *v.* HUME AND HADDOCK

SIR ELIOT EMBER, K.C., today concluded his final speech for the plaintiff in this protracted case: and the aged Mr Justice Codd, shortly to retire, began his summing-up to the jury:

This difficult case, he said, has, I think, no fellow in the history of litigation. For one thing, it is, so far as I know, the first action for defamation in which the words complained of were conveyed by flag-signals at sea. It was suggested, at one point, that the case should be transferred to the Admiralty Court: and, though I had to say no, I have regretted it more than once, so unfamiliar are the waters in which we find ourselves.

The plaintiff, Temper, is the owner and master of the motor-yacht *Perfume II*. The defendant Hume is owner and master of the motor-yacht *Iodine*. The defendant Haddock was a passenger, or rather a guest, in the *Iodine*. Both vessels were cruising in the Mediterranean. At their first encounter in a crowded Italian harbour (X—) there was, it seems, a childish, unseemly and unnecessary altercation between the plaintiff and the defendant Hume. The details do not greatly concern you: but you may well form the opinion, on the evidence you have heard, that the plaintiff was in the wrong, that he was angry and ill-mannered, without due cause: and it is common ground that when the dispute was over he went out of his way to send by boat an insulting message. Mr Hume, it seems, a man of dignity and calm, thought the insult no more worthy of notice than the buzzing of an inflated bluebottle, and throughout behaved with good humour and gentleness. But, his friend and guest, Mr Haddock, less forgiving than the Owner, thought that the last word should not be left where it lay. Hence this action at law.

Mr Haddock, as he told the Court, has long been an admiring student of the International Code of flag-signals. This great Code, begun in a small way by our own Captain Marryat, is one

of the many fine marine affairs in which our country has led the
way, got the nations together, and benefited the world. It is now
so copious and well-planned that almost any thought that one
ship can reasonably wish to express to another is provided
for. It ranges from the short sharp one-flag signals such as the
famous 'Blue Peter' (P), or K – 'You should stop your vessel
instantly' – to such complex queries as:

LVI 'Can you suggest any means whereby my radio apparatus
could be made serviceable?'

Mr Haddock thinks that the Code should be better known,
and more commonly used, than it is, especially by small yachts
on the high seas. Instead, for example, of fumbling vainly round
the dial of a crackling 'wireless', seeking the weather-report in
a foreign language, they should, he says, steer close to the
nearest big steamer (whatever her nationality) and hoist the
two flags:

ZB 'What is the weather forecast for today?'

to which the steamer may reply:

YV 'Heavy weather coming: take necessary precautions.

or:

ATI 'There is no need for alarm.'

or whatever it may be.

Instead, he said, of laborious morsing with lamps which
suddenly cease to work or cannot be clearly distinguished, two
or three gaily coloured flags will often do what is wanted
quicker and better – as, for example:

OVG 'Thank you.'

or:

WAY 'I wish you a pleasant, happy voyage.'

But, he said – and all this is more relevant to the case than you
may at once perceive – practice makes perfect, and custom
grows with use. Accordingly, he has often sent messages to

other yachts and steamers which were not made absolutely necessary by any marine emergency. Not all these communications, it appears, were uniformly well-timed. On one occasion, he confessed, passing the *Queen Elizabeth* in mid-Channel, he hoisted with all solemnity the three groups:

GSX 'Good'
JMR 'Morning'
QUH 'Have you any women on board?'

On another occasion, in wartime, as assistant to the Commodore of a Convoy, he persuaded the Commodore to send to all the merchant ships, in twenty-nine hoists, the whole of the famous peroration of Mr Churchill which begins: 'Let us therefore brace ourselves to our duties' and ends: 'This was their finest hour.' How these communications were received by the masters of the vessels addressed we do not know; but you may think that Mr Temper was not the first mariner to complain of Mr Haddock's fondness for the International Code.

I pass now to the facts of the case. The yachts *Perfume II* and *Iodine* met again frequently, sometimes at sea, sometimes in the many harbours which all yachts seem to visit, sooner or later, in the Western Mediterranean. While passing the *Perfume*, a much slower vessel, Mr Haddock got permission from Mr Hume to 'practise with the flags'; and he hoisted the first signal complained of:

IBQ 'Do you know'
RLO 'Rules of the Road at Sea?'

The plaintiff regarded this as an offensive reference to the former encounter, but could think of no adequate reply in flags. That signal was followed by:

LWV 'Have dead rats been found on board?'

The plaintiff, as you have heard, angrily seized an Aldis lamp and began a strongly-worded reply in morse. The defendant Haddock sent up two hoists:

WX 'I cannot stop to communicate with you.'
LVE 'You should use radio.'

And the *Iodine* steamed ahead.

When the *Perfume* arrived in the crowded little harbour of Y— the *Iodine* was flying, as if by way of welcome, the distinguishing flags of the *Perfume*, and the signal:

L W V 'Have dead rats been found on board?'

The plaintiff called on the *Iodine* and expostulated with Mr Hume. Mr Hume said mildly that Mr Haddock was only 'practising with the flags as usual'. Mr Haddock, on the other hand, said that he had noticed a dead rat on the quayside at Port X—, and, when passing the *Perfume* (who was upwind), he had fancied perhaps, a similar smell. Naturally, he had wondered anxiously whether both vessels were threatened by the same infection. But if the flags offended, they should come down at once. And they did.

But in the next port, Z—, there was more trouble. The Code is rich in medical signals. These are designed to assist one ship to describe to another the condition of a sufferer for whom the first ship requires medical aid. The *Perfume II* was greeted, as usual, with LWV, but, this time, paid no attention. On the second night there was a little party in the *Perfume*, rather noisy, rather late. The next morning there appeared at the yard-arm of the *Iodine*, addressed to *Perfume II*, the following signals which, I must say, look jolly gay and satisfactory to me:

A G W 'Group which follows is a question.'
H G Q 'Headache is very severe.
P C P 'Tongue is coated.'
V G F 'Belly wall is tender.'

The plaintiff again complained.

Mr Albert Haddock's reply to the complaint was simple. He said that that was how he felt that morning, and, as one mariner to another, he was asking a sympathetic question. This time, the flags were not taken down.

At Port W—, after the routine L W V ('Have dead rats been found on board?'), there was a new and singular set of signals:

AGW 'Group which follows is a question.'
VGI 'Breathing is noisy or snorting.'
VGQ 'Have night sweats.'
VGO 'Eyeball burst.'

At Port V—, it was:

AGW 'Group which follows is a question'
PCP 'Tongue is coated'
HGQ 'Headache is very severe'
PJP 'Troubled'
CPT 'By'
ATL 'Alcohol'

And so on.

Now, gentlemen, it is for you and me to analyse and assess the legal significance of this unusual story of the sea. The plaintiff complains of various innuendoes or suggestions in the signals, to wit, that he was unseamanlike, that his ship was plague-ridden or otherwise unhealthy, that he was given to excessive drinking; and he says that he has been held up to hatred, ridicule and contempt in the yachting world. He says that in more than one harbour he was greeted by acquaintances with remarks about 'vermin-vessels' or 'de-ratization'. I have ruled that certain of the flags might bear a defamatory meaning, and you will have to decide whether in all the circumstances they were defamatory or not.

The next question is: By whom were the statements, if defamatory, made? You will probably find that Mr Haddock in each case selected and hoisted the flags: but that he did so with the general permission of Mr Hume, the owner and master of the vessel. In the case of a newspaper the proprietor, the editor and the writer of libellous matter may each and all be sued. But a motor-yacht is not a newspaper (see *The Queen* v. *Robinson* (1891), 2 Q.B.) The nautical experts who testified before us were unanimous that a signal flown at the ship's yard-arm is a signal from the ship, and that, in the absence of fraud or mutiny, the master is alone responsible. It may be, then, that whatever you find in fact, I shall have to strike Mr Haddock out of the action as a matter of law. A further difficulty will then present itself, concerning damages. Whatever you may think about the mind of Mr Haddock, you are not likely to find any evidence of malice in the mind of Mr Hume, who showed gentlemanly forbearance under great provocation. There need, it is true, be no evidence of express malice where a libel is proved, unless the occasion be privileged, which this is not: but you may well think it right to assess different damages for the two defendants, unjust though that may seem. Dear me, what a case!

There remains, for me, at least, perhaps the most delicate question of all. Is this a case of libel or slander? Though the plaintiff complains that his reputation has suffered, he has been able to offer no evidence of any actual damage such as must support, in most cases, an action for slander. He has not suffered professionally or been turned out of a club. Now, the historical but crazy distinction between libel and slander is thus expressed by the good Mr Salmond (I quote the textbook in its third edition (1910) because that was the one in which I learned what I know about torts):

> In *libel* the defamatory statement is made in some permanent and visible form, such as writing, printing, pictures or effigies. In *slander* it is made in spoken words or in some other transitory form, whether visible or audible, such as gestures, hissing, or other inarticulate but significant sounds.[1]

Very well. Where are we now? What are flags? They are 'visible', like writing, printing, or effigies, but unlike words, whispers, or hisses. So, *prima facie*, they must be libel. But are they 'permanent'? Surely not. At sea, the flags remain at the yard-arm till the receiving ship has hoisted the Answering Pendant to the peak, signifying that the signal is understood. Then the flags come down. Gone like the wind. A 'transitory' defamation, surely. But then the plaintiff has sworn that in some ports the flags complained of remained on view *all day*. Should such an exhibition be regarded as transitory or permanent – or, to put the thing fairly – non-transitory? Gentlemen, you now perhaps begin to apprehend the kind of diffi-

1. *Law of Torts* (Stevens and Haynes).

culties which confront me in this case. But I do not know why
I am troubling you with all this: for these are things that I have
to decide alone. The truth is, I am thinking aloud. And, I tell
you what, I am going to make you help me as much as I can.
After all, this may be the last case I try. Get your pencils,
gentlemen: and do try, his Lordship added testily, to keep
awake. We shan't get lunch for another hour and a half.

The Judge left the following questions to the jury:

(*a*) Were any of the signals complained of defamatory?
(*b*) Which?
(*c*) Why?
(*d*) Were there, in fact, any dead rats in M/Y *Perfume II*?
(*e*) If so, does it matter?
(*f*) Do you believe a single word that Mr Haddock says?
(*g*) If 'yes,' give examples.
(*h*) Between ourselves, don't you think the plaintiff is a fairly
unsympathetic character?
(*i*) Have you the faintest idea, after all my laborious discourse:
    (i) What is the difference between libel and slander?
    (ii) Why?
(*j*) If 'yes', would you say that flag-signals were:
    (i) Transitory?
    (ii) Non-transitory?
(*k*) And, if you were in my place, though, mind you, this is my
job, not yours, would you say that this was a case of libel or
slander?
(*l*) (i) Why?
    (ii) Why not?
(*m*) What damages:
    (i) Against Mr Hume?
    (ii) Against Mr Haddock?
(*n*) You may have to find for the plaintiff: but, honestly, if you
were me, would you give him any costs?
(*o*) By the way, I forgot to ask you – do you think that the plaintiff's reputation has suffered?
(*p*) If 'yes', does this upset you?
(*q*) Now will you retire, please? And come back soon.

The jury retired, for seventeen hours. On their return, the

Foreman said: My Lord, we are a little confused. We disagree on almost every particular.

His Lordship: Well done. I think you are quite right.

Sir Eliot Ember, for the plaintiff, asked for costs.

The Judge: Well, no. You see, I have decided to strike Mr Haddock out of the action as he was not the master of the ship. And Mr Hume has behaved very decently throughout. So I am afraid the plaintiff will have to pay all the costs.

Sir Eliot: If your Lordship pleases.

Sir Ronald Rutt: Shall we have a new trial?

The Judge: Not before me. Why don't you appeal? Your father would love this case.

3 October 1951

Note: See 'End of a Nonsense', page 111.

What are Snails?

COWFAT *v.* WHEEDLE

(*Before Mr Justice Wool*)

THE hearing of this case, which raises a legal point of far-reaching importance to gardeners and horticulturists, was concluded today.

Mrs Cowfat, who appears *in forma pauperis*, is suing her neighbour, Mrs Wheedle, for alleged trespass and damage to property. Plaintiff and defendant live in adjoining houses in the suburb of West Munsey. Both are keen gardeners, and plaintiff alleges that defendant has made a practice of throwing snails and slugs over the dividing wall, thus damaging Mrs Cowfat's plants and injuring her chances of gaining prizes at the West Munsey flower-show.

Mrs Cowfat's cross-examination was continued this morning. The contrast between this witness's downright diction and counsel's polished phrases caused much comment.

Mrs Cowfat : I seen 'er done it – see?

Mr Swoot (counsel for the defence) : You say you saw the defendant transferring snails from her garden to yours?

Witness : I tell you I seen 'er done it. Can't speak plainer than that, can I?

Counsel : I put it to you that your story is a tissue of fabrications.

Witness : I seen 'er done it. And my clean 'olly-'ocks nothin' but 'oles from that day to this. More like a sponge, they was.

Counsel : Will you tell my lord what time of day it was that you saw the defendant engaged in this manner?

Witness : Ask 'er 'oo it was won first prize for 'olly-'ocks, Mister.

Counsel : Answer the question, please, Mrs Cowfat. What time of day was this?

Witness : Night-time, of course. Think she'd have the face to do it in the daylight? Nasty, creeping thing . . .

Counsel : Then it would be dark, Mrs Cowfat?

Witness : Dark? I should say so. Gone half-past ten, because I'd 'eard Wheedle come back from the pub, singing somethink awful . . .

Counsel : Very dark?

Witness : You're right, Mister. And she's a dark one. If I was to tell you all I know . .

The Judge : You are here to tell all you know, Mrs Cowfat, provided it is relevant.

Witness : Well, then, ask 'er what Wheedle said to the lodger the night he put 'im outside. Ask 'er 'oo it was fed 'er two cats, night and morning, when she went off Whitsun . . .

Counsel : One moment, Mrs Cowfat. You have told my lord that it was very dark. And yet it was not so dark that you were unable to see the defendant throwing snails over the wall?

Witness : I seen 'er done it.

Counsel : On the 18th May did you reprove defendant for putting salt on the snails in her garden?

Witness : That's right. Nasty cruel thing! Standing watching 'em shrivel. That's what put 'er against me.

Counsel : You disapprove of that method of immobilizing a garden pest, Mrs Cowfat?

Witness : I seen 'er done it.

Counsel : Will you tell my Lord how you dispose of the snails in your own garden?

Witness : Never were no snails in my garden, Mister, not before Flo Wheedle began 'er dirty games.

Counsel : Oh! So there were no snails in your garden, Mrs Cowfat, prior to the 14th of June?

Witness : You 'eard what I said.

Counsel : A very remarkable garden, Mrs Cowfat, in its complete freedom from destructive gasteropods?

Witness : Remarkable? You oughter seen it last summer – first prize 'olly-'ocks, sea-kale, and lettuce. *And* a second for geraniums.

Counsel : To what, Mrs Cowfat, do you attribute your immunity from snails?

Witness : Patent fertilizers, Mister. Turns their stummicks and they don't come a second time.

Counsel : I put it to you, Mrs Cowfat, that your immunity is susceptible of a more sinister explanation?

Witness : Pardon?

Counsel : I suggest to you that for many years past it has been your habit to transfer your snails to your neighbours' gardens?

A woman in the body of the Court : That's right.

Witness : Oh, you wicked man! Oh, how dare you! Say that again, Liz Roberts, and I'll tear your eyes out! (*Witness here became highly excited.*)

The Judge : Please control yourself.

Witness : All right, guv'nor. Only you wait till I get at 'er – see?

Counsel : Would you say, Mrs Cowfat, that the snail was an animal *ferae naturae?*

Mr Bottle (counsel for the plaintiff) : Milord, I object!

Mr Swoot : If me learned friend will have a little patience . . .

Mr Bottle : The witness cannot be expected . . .

The Judge : I don't *quite* see where this is leading us, Mr Swoot.

Mr Swoot : Milord, it is the defendant's case that she did not in fact throw snails into the plaintiff's garden, and in the alternative that, if she did, they were snails which, so far as there can be property in snails, were the property of the plaintiff, and, thirdly, that they were animals *ferae naturae* which the defendant had not brought onto her own property and therefore was under no obligation to keep upon her own property. Milord, in the case of *Rylands* v. *Fletcher* . . .

The Judge : Dear, dear! *Must* we have *Rylands* v. *Fletcher?*

Mr Bottle : Milord, at the proper time I shall have a good deal to say about that case, which, in my submission, milord, is on all fours, milord, with the present . . .

Mr Swoot : Milord, in that case it was held that a person who keeps a wild beast or dangerous thing upon his property is answerable for the consequences if that animal or thing escapes and does damage to the property of his neighbour; but, milord . . .

Witness : 'Ere, Mister . . .

The Judge : Do you distinguish, Mr Swoot, between a destructive mammal and a destructive gasteropod?

Mr Swoot : No, milord. But I distinguish between the cases. Milord, if my client had kept a tiger on her property she would be answerable for the consequences of its escape. But if a wandering tiger, milord, over which she had no control, were to come upon her property, I submit, milord, she would be entitled, milord, to take any steps which suggested themselves in order to induce it to leave her property, even, I submit, milord, if she were to open the gate dividing her property from her neighbour's and persuade the animal by gestures to depart through that gate . . .

The Judge : An interesting point, Mr Swoot, but does it arise?

Witness : Oy!

The Judge : Be quiet.

Witness : 'Ere, guv'nor, am I giving evidence or 'im? I seen 'er done it – wish I may die!

Mr Swoot : Milord, I rely upon *Swabe* v. *The Ecclesiastical Commissioners*. Milord, the snails in defendant's garden were not brought there by her and are not under her control, being at liberty at any time to cross the wall into the plaintiff's garden. Milord, I ask you to rule that the snail is an animal *ferae naturae* . . .

The Judge : What has Mr Bottle to say to that?

Witness : I seen 'er done it.

After further legal argument, his Lordship said: Mr Swoot, you have conducted your argument with marked ability. The legal points involved are of considerable importance and complexity. The evidence discloses a long-standing feud between two neighbours, who, as horticulturists, are naturally anxious to rid their properties of the destructive snail, which I hold to be an animal *ferae naturae*. It appears that the plaintiff, whose evidence was almost wholly unsatisfactory, has for long made a practice of transferring or urging her snails into defendant's garden, since she has a feminine shrinking from the taking of life herself. The defendant, less sensitive, has destroyed them with salt, admittedly a painful and humiliating end. The plaintiff made adverse comments upon this practice, whereupon the defendant, according to the plaintiff, transferred them to her neighbour's property, from which, we may suspect, they were again ejected. We have a picture, therefore, of a state of affairs in which the snails of this neighbourhood have been changing their location with a rapidity to which they are quite unaccustomed. It is not too much to say that in West Munsey Villas it rains snails. If the evidence is to be believed, the snail war has spread beyond the original parties. The plaintiff suggests that many of her neighbours, taking the defendant's side, have conspired to collect their snails and deposit them in quite unreasonable numbers upon her hollyhocks. There are concerted operations, there are night expeditions, there are watchers at windows. The question for me is, Does this deplorable state of affairs disclose a cause of action-at-law? I find that it does not. A person may lawfully frighten the birds from his orchard, though he knows that as soon as they leave his own property they must enter upon his neighbour's; and similarly he is entitled to urge the wild snail with threats, entreaties, or loud noises into his neighbour's garden. Mr Bottle asked me to draw a distinction between the persuasion or intimidation of a snail and the deliberate throwing of a snail; but that distinction is too fine for me. I must not be understood to say that defendant is entitled to pelt the plaintiff with snails; but trespass to property and trespass to the person are two different things, and in the absence of the latter I hold that the property owner may dispose of his snails in what way he pleases. The action therefore must be dismissed. I am told that this decision will cause grave suspicion, unrest, and enmity in our towns and suburbs, but I cannot help that. It is the law.

28 May 1930

Is Magna Carta Law?

THE hearing of this appeal, which raised a novel point of law, was concluded in the High Court today.

Mr Justice Lugg (delivering judgment): In this case the defendant, one Haddock, is appealing on a case stated from a conviction by a Court of Summary Jurisdiction under the Transport and Irritation of Motorists Act, 1920. The defendant was summoned before the Gerrard Street magistrates on a charge of causing an obstruction in a public thoroughfare by leaving his motor-car unattended for two hours and ten minutes on the night of 31 December 1925.

The case for the defence was that the motor-car had not in fact caused an obstruction, and it was sworn in evidence that the road was not in fact a thoroughfare at all in the ordinary sense of the term, but a short blind alley terminating in a blank wall, against which wall the motor-car was left with the lights burning, according to law; and the police-officer who made the charge was unable to say that during the period in question he had seen any other vehicle, or indeed any other human being, enter the thoroughfare which the defendant's vehicle was obstructing. The magistrates, however, very properly, as I think, brushed aside this somewhat frivolous defence and ordered Mr Haddock to pay a fine of two pounds and the costs of the prosecution, with additional costs of one pound for conducting his defence in rhymed couplets.

Mr Haddock has now appealed on a point of law, which I confess is novel to me, under the fourteenth chapter of Magna Carta. The fourteenth chapter of Magna Carta is directed against excessive fines, and provides that:

A freeman shall not be amerced [that is, fined] for a small fault, but after the manner of the fault, and for a great fault after the greatness thereof. . .

And it has been powerfully argued by Sir Rowland Wash that

since there is nothing in the Irritation of Motorists Act or in any other statute repealing or suspending this particular chapter, the Irritation of Motorists Act must be read in conjunction with that chapter; that the fine of two pounds is excessive and not 'after the manner of the fault', which is a small one, and that it ought to be reduced.

Now, in private, and even more in public life, there is no doubt that persons are accustomed to speak loosely of Magna Carta as the enduring foundation of what are known as the liberties of the subject, and to assume that that Charter is as potent a measure today as at the time of its origin. But, if we examine the Great Charter, as I did for the first time in bed this morning, we are led towards the conclusion that, if this is the foundation of the liberties of the subject, then these liberties are not so numerous as is commonly supposed; for out of the thirty-seven chapters of Magna Carta at least twenty-three have become obsolete, or have been abolished by later legislation, while among the fourteen which are not definitely extinguished there are at least as many for the benefit of the Crown as for the benefit of the subject, and the remainder have only a precarious existence, if any. In Chapter 8, for example, and Chapter 18, which begins:

If any that holdeth of us lay-fee to die, and our sheriff or bailiff do show our letters-patent of our summons for debt, which the dead man did owe to us, it shall be lawful to our sheriff or bailiff to attach and inroll all the goods and chattels of the dead. . .

it is laid down very clearly that debts owing to Government Departments take precedence over all other debts; but it would be difficult to found upon these chapters any extravagant description of Magna Carta as the fountain of individual freedom. Again, the ordinary citizen will extract no particular satisfaction from the assurance of Chapter 23, that:

All weirs from henceforth shall be utterly pulled down in the Thames and Medway, and through all England, but only by the sea-coasts.

Macaulay said that the blood of the uttermost settler in the northern deserts of Australia flowed more freely in his veins as he lay beneath the Southern Cross and studied by its light the unforgettable conclusion of Chapter 29:

To no man will we sell, to no man deny, to no man delay, justice or right.

But we in this Court are well aware that these undertakings have very little relation to the harsh facts of experience. All that can be said is that much justice is sold at quite reasonable prices, and that there are still many citizens who can afford to buy the more expensive brands. If a man has no money at all he can get justice for nothing: but if he has any money he will have to buy justice, and even then may have to go without right (for the two expressions are not always synonymous). Indeed, there is something to be said for selling, denying, and delaying some sorts of justice. The thoughtful observer will distinguish between litigation which is a genuine pursuit of justice, such as a prosecution for embezzlement or murder, and the litigation which is a mere luxury, hobby, disease, profession, or species of blackmail, such as are many libel actions and nearly all suits for breach of promise of marriage. The proper business of the Courts could not be conducted if every citizen who conceived himself insulted could immediately bring an action for defamation without cost to himself. Fish-porters and charwomen pass through life exchanging frank opinions about each other's characters, but never, so far as is known, feel the itch to bring an action for defamation. They could not if they wished: so it might be said that justice is denied them. But they do not wish: and no great hardship is suffered. As for the delay, there can be no dignity without what appears to the thoughtless to be delay. But, beyond that, there will always be a certain delay in the Courts so long as the Crown and Parliament decline to equip them with an adequate supply of judges and shorthand-writers. At all events, the statutory pledges of the Crown set out above mean very little today.

Again, in Chapter 30, it is laid down that:

All merchants shall have their safe and sure conduct to depart out of England, to come into England, to tarry in and go through

England as well by land as by water, to buy and sell, without any manner of evil tolls (i.e. extortions) by the old and rightful customs.

But he would be a bold advocate who contended that this was an accurate statement of the law, or, at any rate, the practice of the land today. No man, merchant or no, can depart out of England, come into England, tarry in England, or buy or sell without all manner of tolls, extortions, and hindrances by the Crown, which is very right and proper but is not Magna Carta.

Again, it was argued before me that at least that portion of Chapter 29 still has effect, which reads:

Nor will we proceed against a freeman, nor condemn him, but by lawful judgment of his peers or by the law of the land.

But it was proved in evidence that in fact this method of condemning the freeman is the exception rather than the rule, and it was suggested that this portion of Magna Carta must be interpreted in the light of recent statutes, so that it reads:

Nor will we proceed against a freeman, nor condemn him, but by lawful judgment of his peers or by the law of the land, or Government Departments, or Marketing Boards, or Impregnable Monopolies, or Trade Unions, or Fussy Societies, or Licensing Magistrates, or officious policemen, or foolish regulations by a Clerk in the Home Office made and provided.

And in fact in the present case the defendant was not proceeded against by the law of the land, but by regulations; nor was he condemned by his peers, but by a policeman who expected half a crown, and by a magistrate antipathetical to the motorist.

Now, Lord Mildew said in *Klaxon* v. *Great Western Railway* (1871) 2 Q.B.: 'The whole is greater than the part', and this is undoubtedly the law. So if, on a detailed examination of a statute, as of a bicycle, it is found that nearly every part is obsolete or has been destroyed, there is a strong presumption that the whole has for practical purposes ceased to exist. And in this case I am satisfied that so little of Magna Carta is left that nothing of Magna Carta is left, and therefore that chapter on which the appellant relies must be taken to have perished with the others.

The appellant has done his country an ill service in raising this point, for, but for his rash act, generations of English orators might have continued in the fond belief that Magna Carta was still the abiding bulwark of our liberties, and for that act I shall order him to pay a further fine of five pounds.[1] But it is no part of my duty to conceal the truth, and I am compelled to declare with some reluctance that Magna Carta is no longer law.

The appeal was dismissed.

16 February 1927

1. He recalled how, in the chancel of Tewkesbury Abbey, he once came across a stone to one of the barons of Magna Carta on which were the words *'Magna Carta est lex. Deinde caveat rex.'* ('Magna Carta is the law, and let the king look out.') (Mr Stanley Baldwin in Westminster Hall, 4 July 1935)

The Expert Witness

(*Before Mr Justice Wool*)

THERE was a dramatic climax today to Sir Ethelred Rutt's cross-examination of Mr Stanley in the Canary Guano case. Sir Ethelred, in his opening speech, described Mr Stanley as 'the vilest thug in Christendom'. Troops lined the approaches to the Court, and there were some sharp exchanges between Sir Ethelred Rutt and Sir Humphrey Codd, in which both the famous advocates constantly thumped on the desk, raised their eyebrows, and blew their noses. Sir Ethelred's brief is marked four thousand pounds, with 'refreshers' of two hundred pounds a day, and it is the general opinion in legal circles that the case will never finish. Had the defendant company been unable to secure his services, it is calculated that the case would have been clearly intelligible from the beginning, and in all probability would have been concluded in a day.

Sir Humphrey Codd (concluding his examination-in-chief): And, in fact, Mr Stanley, the gist of your evidence is that there are, in fact, *no* vitamins in canary guano?
Mr Stanley: That is so.

Sir Ethelred Rutt then rose to cross-examine. Three well-dressed women fainted and were thrown out.

Sir Ethelred: You are Mr Stanley?
Witness: That is my name.
Sir Ethelred: But of course, Mr Stanley, your name is *not* Stanley at all – but Moss?
Witness: Yes.
Sir Ethelred: Would it be fair to suggest that before the Great War your name was Moses?
Witness: Yes.

Sir Ethelred: And before the South African war was your name Finkelstein?

Witness: Yes.

Sir Ethelred: What was your name before the Crimean war?

Witness: I forget.

Sir Ethelred: You forget? *Very* well. And you appear as an expert witness for the plaintiff?

Witness: Yes.

Sir Ethelred: Exactly. Now, Mr Finkelstein, in your opinion, suppose a ton of canary guano is shipped at Hamburg f.o.b. Cardiff, adding two pounds of the best beef suet, and making the necessary adjustments for the Swiss Exchange, what would be the effect on a young girl? Just tell the jury that, will you?

Witness: That would depend on the voltage.

The Judge (who took long-hand notes throughout the proceedings): That – would – depend – on – the – voltage. Go on.

Sir Ethelred: And that was on the 22nd, I think?

The Judge: My note says 'Bees-wax'.

Sir Ethelred: Milord, with great submission – that was the *last* case, I think.

The Judge: Oh! But what about the charter-party?

Sir Ethelred: I beg your pardon, milord. I am very much obliged to you, milord . . . So that, *in fact*, Mr Stanley, in the case of a widow, and counting thirteen to the dozen, the price of canary guano would vary with the weather in the ratio of 2 to 1, or 1 to 2 in the northern hemisphere?

Witness: That is so. Except, of course, at high water.

Sir Ethelred: Except at high water. Quite, quite. I understand that. Milord, I don't know whether the jury follow that.

The Judge (to the jury): You hear what the witness says? There are thirteen to a dozen in the case of a widow, except at high water in the northern hemisphere.

Sir Ethelred: Milord, with great respect, that is not *quite* . . .

The Judge (sternly): Sir Ethelred, you go too far!

Sir Ethelred: I beg your pardon, milord. I am very much obliged to you, milord. (*To the witness*) Have you got varicose veins, Mr Stanley?

Witness (warmly): No!

Sir Ethelred : I put it to you, Mr Stanley, that you *have* got varicose veins?

Witness : Must I answer that, your honour?

Sir Humphrey : Milord, I object. Me learned friend . . .

Sir Ethelred : Milord, I do submit – I have a reason for asking, milord.

Sir Humphrey :
Sir Ethelred : } Milord!

The two famous advocates here engaged in a violent altercation in undertones.

The Judge : Without anticipating anything I may have to say at a later stage, and subject to anything which may be disclosed in evidence next year, and bearing in mind the relations of the parties, and without prejudice to the issue of forgery, and *prima facie* and *statu quo*, and not forgetting the Boat Race, I think it right to say that so far as I understand the law (and, of course, I am a mere child in Sir Ethelred's hands) I shall at a suitable moment be prepared to say that the question is relevant and should be answered, subject to the consideration that this sentence has now continued so long that it may be arguable that the law has altered in the meantime.

Sir Ethelred : I am very much obliged, milord.

The Judge : But I don't see where it is leading us. (*To the witness*) *Have* you got varicose veins?

Witness : Well, milord, it's like this . . .

The Judge (impatiently) : Come, come, my man, don't beat about the bush! Either you have varicose veins or you have not.

Witness : Yes, milord, I have.

The Judge : Very well, then (*writing*) 'Do – you – suffer – from – varicose – veins?' *Answer :* 'I – do.' Now then, Sir Ethelred, do let us get *on*!

Sir Ethelred (to the witness) : Now take your mind back to the 22nd of May 1884. On the 22nd of May 1884, Mr Stanley – milord, I have rather a delicate question to put to the witness. Perhaps your Lordship would prefer me to commit it to writing?

The Judge: By 'delicate', Sir Ethelred, I take it that you mean '*in*delicate'? (*Laughter*)

Sir Ethelred: Yes, milord.

The Judge: Then I am afraid we must have the question.

Sir Ethelred: Milord, there is a woman on the jury, and in view of the delicate character of the question, I propose, with your permission, to write it down in invisible ink and hand it to the witness in a sealed box.

The Judge: Very well, Sir Ethelred. This is great fun.

Sir Ethelred then wrote rapidly on a piece of paper and handed it to the witness, who was unable to conceal his emotion. The question and the answer were then examined by counsel, tied up with string, and carefully disinfected, after which his Lordship carried them to the jury-box, where the foreman unpacked them and fainted. Meanwhile, to Sir Ethelred's obvious annoyance, public interest in the case was steadily mounting; there was a baton charge in the corridor outside the court, and in the streets the troops were compelled to fire a volley over the heads of the crowd.

Sir Ethelred: So on the 22nd May 1884, Mr Stanley, did your wife bear you a male child?

Witness: She did.

Sir Ethelred: Was that your *fourth* wife?

Witness: No.

Sir Ethelred: Ah! Would it be fair to say that you have committed alimony?

Witness: Never!

Sir Ethelred: I put it to you that the suggestion I have put to you is consistent with the hypothesis that the answers you have given are easily distinguishable from the true facts? Yes or No?

Witness: It is a lie.

Sir Ethelred: Do you smoke in the bath?

Sir Humphrey: I object.

Sir Ethelred: I put to it you that you do smoke in the bath.

Witness: No.

Sir Ethelred: I suggest that you are a bully and a black-guard.

Witness: Nothing of the sort. Don't browbeat me, sir!

The Judge: Now then, Mr Stanley, you mustn't get into an altercation. Answer the question.

Witness: He didn't ask me a question. He made a statement.

The Judge (sternly): Mr Stanley, this is not far removed from contempt of Court. It is my duty to protect learned counsel. Now answer the learned counsel's question.

Witness: I am sorry, milord.

Sir Ethelred: I put it to you that you are a bully and a blackguard.

Witness: No.

Sir Ethelred: Very well. Did you stay at the Grand Hotel, Palermo, in September 1911 with a woman purporting to be your wife?

Witness: Yes.

Sir Ethelred: Was she your wife?

Witness: Yes.

Sir Ethelred: On the evening of the 11th of September were you in your private room with a woman?

Witness: Very likely.

Sir Ethelred: Be careful, Mr Stanley – the house was being watched, you know. At nine p.m. did you draw the blinds in your private room?

Witness: Very likely.

Sir Ethelred: Ah! So you drew the blinds? Will you tell the Court and jury why you drew the blinds?

Witness: To annoy the watchers.

The Judge: If you are not careful, Mr Stanley, you will be placed in the Tower.

Sir Ethelred: Would it surprise you to learn that this letter which you wrote on the 30th May is in your own handwriting? Yes or No?

Witness: No.

Sir Ethelred: Did you know a Mr Trout who died of indigestion?

Witness: Yes.

Sir Ethelred : Then do you still say that you do not smoke in the bath?

Witness : Yes.

Sir Ethelred : I suggest that you do smoke in the bath.

Witness : No.

Sir Ethelred : I put it to you that you smoked in the bath last April.

Witness : Very well. Have it your own way, Sir Ethelred.

Sir Ethelred : And you have committed alimony?

Witness : No.

Sir Ethelred : Why not?

Witness : I resent the innuendo.

Sir Ethelred : Is that your mentality, Mr Moss?

Witness : Leave my mentality alone.

Sir Ethelred (sternly) : Answer the question!

Sir Humphrey : Really, milord, I must object.

The Judge : I don't think the mentality of the witness is admissible, Sir Ethelred.

Sir Ethelred : Very well, milord. At Palermo, in September, there would be good sea-bathing?

Witness : Yes.

Sir Ethelred : Would it be fair to say that you bathed at Palermo?

Witness : Yes.

Sir Ethelred : In company with this woman who accompanied you?

Witness : Yes.

Sir Ethelred : Mixed bathing?

Witness : Certainly. My wife is a woman.

Sir Ethelred : Of course, Mr Moss, I don't suggest that there is anything wrong in mixed bathing.

Witness : Then why did you refer to it?

Sir Ethelred : Milord, I claim the protection of the Court.

The Judge : Mr Moss, I am here to protect learned counsel, and I will not have them insulted. It is little I am allowed to do in these proceedings, but at least I can do that. Sir Ethelred is paid a great deal of money for cross-examining you, and the longer he cross-examines you the longer will the case continue and the more will Sir Ethelred be paid. It is therefore very selfish of you to take the bread out of his mouth by objecting to his little excursions into fancy. Moreover, he has the mind of a child, and has not the least idea how people really behave. He gets his ideas from French plays and detective stories, and you must admit that he is most entertaining. Moreover, he is very sensitive, so please answer his questions kindly, and don't upset him.

Sir Ethelred: I am very much obliged to your lordship. Is three litres of acilysalic acid, Mr Stanley, a greater or a lesser proportion than the same quantity of gin?

Witness: It is not.

Sir Ethelred: I put it to you that it is.

Witness: It is a lie.

Sir Ethelred: What was your name before it was Finkel-stein?

Witness: Rutt.

The Judge: Did you say 'Pratt'?

Witness: 'Rutt', milord – RUTT.

The Judge: Oh – Wright.

Sir Ethelred at this point seemed overcome, and for a moment he was unable to proceed. The Judge ordered the windows to be opened.

Sir Ethelred: Now tell the jury this. What were you doing on the night of the 30th June 1891?

Witness: I was in bed.

Sir Ethelred: Did you, on the 30th June 1891, deposit your infant child on the doorstep of the Foundling Hospital?

Sir Humphrey: Really, milord, I must object. Me learned friend is not entitled . . .

Sir Ethelred: Milord, my instructions are, milord . . .

Sir Humphrey: Milord, me learned friend . . .

Sir Ethelred: Me learned friend, milord . . .

Both counsel here talked at the same time, exchanging angry glances, thumping on the desk, and scratching each other.

The Judge: I think I must allow the question. (*To the witness*) Did you, in fact, dispose of your child in the manner suggested?

Witness: I did, milord.

Sir Ethelred: I see. Would it be true to say, Mr Moss, that at that date your son had a piece of red flannel tied round his middle?

Witness: It would.

Sir Ethelred: Exactly. Now take your time, Mr Stanley, and be very careful how you answer. Had the child, or had he not, *in fact*, a little mole on the left elbow?

Sir Humphrey: Really, milord, with great respect, milord, me learned friend has no right, milord . . .

The Judge: That seems to me a perfectly proper question, Sir Humphrey.

Sir Ethelred: Well, Mr Stanley?

Witness (with emotion): God forgive me, he had. My little boy!

Sir Ethelred: Then you, Mr Stanley, are my father.

Witness: My son! My son!

Sir Ethelred here vaulted over the bar and embraced the witness, who seemed much affected by this dramatic reunion.

The Judge: Is there any precedent for this proceeding, Sir Ethelred?

Sir Ethelred: No, milord.

The Judge: Then do not do it again.[1]

The hearing was adjourned.

Note: It is 'contempt of Court' to make faces at a cross-examining K.C. (*In re Fitzmaurice*) but not (*Martin's Case*) at a solicitor's clerk. A member of the jury may powder her nose in the box but not use lipstick or (*Rex* v. *Salmon*) eat oranges. And see *Marrable* v. *Rowntree,* where the jury, on being discharged, sang 'For he's a jolly good fellow', and were committed for contempt.

1. But see Lord Mildew in *Doggett* v. *Port of London Authority*: 'There is no precedent for anything until it is done for the first time.'

The Fortune-Tellers

REX *v.* 'THE COLONEL', 'SEER', 'PATHFINDER',
'OLD JOE', 'AJAX', GILBEY, WALLACE, AND
THE RACING CORRESPONDENT OF *THE TIMES*
NEWSPAPER

(*Before Mr Justice Wool*)

AT the Old Bailey today the Attorney-General, Sir Anthony
Platt, opened the case for the prosecution in the Fortune-
Telling Case. He said:

Milord, the prisoners in the dock are charged under Section
4 of the Vagrancy Act 1824, with pretending or professing to
tell fortunes. Under that Act, milord, any persons using any
subtle craft, means, or device, by palmistry, or otherwise, to
deceive the people are rogues and vagabonds and punishable
with imprisonment and hard labour. In a previous case today
a woman named Sibylla was tried and convicted for pretending
to tell fortunes by means of palmistry; yesterday a gipsy
woman was sent to prison for professing to tell fortunes by
means of playing-cards. The prisoners in the dock are charged
under the same section of the same statute; and, though in
appearance they are more respectable than the individuals I
have referred to, they are equally obliged to obey the law, and
the essence of the offence with which they are charged is the
same.

Milord, the essence of that offence is the deception of the
people by a person pretending to have the power to predict the
future. The laws of England have for many centuries regarded
with jealous suspicion any claim of that kind. Our judges and
legislators, knowing by long experience how difficult it is for
mortal man to give a correct and accurate account of what took
place only a few weeks ago, will not believe that mortal man
can give correct accounts of that which has not yet taken place

at all.[1] By a statute of Queen Elizabeth's reign, repealed in 1863, false prophecies were punishable as misdemeanours, as raising enthusiastic jealousies among the people and terrifying them with imaginary fears. If the prophet Isaiah were to appear in London today he would be at once arrested. Foresight, milord, is a quality which wins applause for the citizen, provided that he looks forward to his own future only and does not pretend to see into other people's. The distinction is perhaps a fine one ...

The Judge : Not at all, Mr Attorney. It is very simple. I may look into my own bedroom, but I must not look into a lady's. (*Laughter*)

The Attorney-General : Ha! Very good, milord. A matter of property.

The Judge : No, no – propriety. (*Laughter*)

The Attorney-General : Your lordship is exceedingly witty and well informed. But, with great respect, milord, that is not exactly the basis of the offence; otherwise it would be equally dangerous to give an account of other people's pasts ...

The Judge : It very often is. (*Laughter*)

The Attorney-General : Milord, the prisoners in that dock have for many years been earning a livelihood by pretending to tell the fortunes or predict the futures, not of men and women, but of horses. They vary in method, in prose style, in confidence, and in popularity; but they have this in common, that they do hold out to the people who read their newspapers that they are able, by some special gift or power or information, to predict with something approaching to certainty the future conduct and fortunes of race-horses. It will be proved in evidence, milord, that for these predictions, which are issued daily – even, I regret to say, milord, on the Sabbath Day – they receive money; and that numbers of the people are deceived by their pretensions, act upon their predictions, and suffer damage. Some of the prisoners, milord, to take an example,

1. See *Simon's Case* (1731), in which the prisoner travelled about the country crying, 'Your food will cost you more.' He was whipped at Pennyfields and stood in the pillory at Chancery Lane for three days.

have already predicted that a horse named Diolite will win the Derby.

The Judge : What is the Derby?

The Attorney-General : Milord, the Derby is one of the most popular horse competitions, in which colts of . . .

The Attorney-General here conferred with the Solicitor to the Treasury and continued: Milord, I am instructed that colts of the age of three years take part in this race, and that considerable sums of money are wagered upon the event.

The Judge : Is it one of these trotting-races?

The Attorney-General : No, milord, it is a galloping-race. Now, milord, in the eyes of the law there is no distinction between a man and a horse . . .

The Judge : Have you any authority for that, Sir Anthony?

The Attorney-General : I mean, milord, for fortune-telling purposes. The woman Sibylla was sent to prison for telling a police-officer that he would have good fortune and travel abroad, that a large sum of money was coming to him, that he would go a long journey and meet a dark lady in a foreign capital. Can it be said that that man is less deceitful and dangerous who tells the people that such-and-such a horse will start from a given place at a given time, travel a given journey, and arrive at a given destination in advance of thirty other horses selected from a large number for their swiftness and staying power? The jury may well think that the latter set of prognostications is the more difficult to justify. For the conduct and career of the average man obey certain laws of probability and reason . . .

The Judge : Did you say 'man' or 'woman'? (*Laughter*)

The Attorney-General : 'Man', milord. (*Laughter*) Most of us, for example, have, in fact, gone a long journey and met a dark lady in a foreign capital. But the behaviour of horses, as the expert witnesses will presently testify, appears to conform to no known laws, whether of reason, psychology, or mathematical probability. Their actions are impulsive, capricious, and incalculable; their health is delicate, their nervous system easily disturbed, and their moral sense negligible. The merest straw is sufficient to upset their temperaments and the hopes which human beings have formed concerning them. And this is especially true of those highly bred and sensitive animals who compete professionally in the public horse-races. We shall hear in the course of this case, milord, of certain horses called 'favourites' – horses, milord, which because of their parentage, their past performances and the known ability of the jockeys who are to ride them, are confidently expected by a majority of the persons interested to defeat all the competitors in this race or that. But we shall also hear that it is a comparatively rare event for the so-called 'favourite' to finish first; and in fact, milord, he (or she) has been known to finish among the last, so many are the chances and accidents which in a race between horses may disappoint even the unanimous expectations of a people. Yet these are the animals, milord, whose fortunes the individuals in that dock have pretended to tell.

The Judge: Do you say, Mr Attorney, that the prisoners have never made a prediction which proved to be correct?

The Attorney-General: No, milord; there have been cases . . .

The Judge: Then, if, the essence of the offence is the deceit, these cases must be placed to their credit.

The Attorney-General: No, milord; with great respect, milord, they are an aggravation of the offence. For the rare occasions on which the prisoners are right tend to persuade the people that they have special powers and will be right again; and, in fact, milord, these occasions are carefully recorded and advertised for the purpose of encouraging that belief. Boastful placards, milord, such as 'Who gave you that Nap?' . . .

The Judge: What is a 'Nap'?

The Attorney-General conferred with the Treasury Solicitor.

The Attorney-General: A 'Nap', I am instructed, milord, is a prediction made with such exceptional confidence that the person addressed is advised to go 'Nap' upon the indicated horse; that is, milord, to put his shirt on it . . .

The Judge: Is that what is meant by a horse carrying weights?

The Attorney-General: No, milord.

The Judge (impatiently): It is all Greek to me. Go on, Sir Anthony. Please don't waste time.

The Attorney-General: Milord, at a later stage I shall ask you to find different degrees of guilt among the prisoners. The prisoner from *The Times* newspaper, for example,[1] has never, I believe, gone so far as to offer his readers a 'Nap'. His method is, milord, to discuss the history and idiosyncrasies of the various horses in prose of a thoughtful and delicate style; and in conclusion he will write, after a hint of diffidence, some such phrase as, 'I must therefore take Beetroot to win.' A more modest formula, milord, than the 'Nap'; but in essence, according to the prosecution, it is the same, that is to say, a prediction that Beetroot will be successful, a pretended telling of Beetroot's fortune. Indeed, milord, there is some evidence that the restraint and quietness of this man's prophetic utterances have induced in the public a greater confidence than the boastful purveyors of 'Naps' and 'Doubles' have been able to do; that is to say, the section of the public which he addresses are made ready to bet, and therefore, in the end, to suffer damage. Nevertheless, milord, you may be prepared to consider, in mitigation of sentence, the care and beauty of this man's prose.

The Judge: What exactly is a bet? What is the procedure?

The Attorney-General had not concluded his address when the Court adjourned.

21 May 1930

1. Mr R. C. Lyle.

Is Homer Obscene?

REX *v.* THE HEADMASTER OF ETON COLLEGE

At Windsor today, before a full Bench of magistrates, a serious charge was made against the Headmaster of Eton, a clergyman, who appeared to feel his position acutely. Police-Constable Boot gave evidence in support of the charge, which was preferred under the Obscene Publications Act 1857, commonly known as Lord Campbell's Act.

Constable Boot: On the fifth of this month, acting under instructions, I proceeded with a special warrant to the premises known as Eton College and made a thorough search of the same. I found and seized there a number of books which in my opinion were of an obscene character. Defendant admitted that the said books were kept on the premises to be 'sold, distributed, lent, or otherwise published' within the meaning of the Act, to the students under his charge, who are from thirteen to nineteen years of age, your worship.

The Attorney-General: Have you carefully perused the said books?

Constable Boot: I have.

Sir Ethelred Rutt (for the defence): Your worship, I have here a hundred and forty-nine professors and schoolmasters who are prepared to go into that box and swear that the volumes in question have not the character suggested.

The Chairman: What is the use of that? The defendant himself is a schoolmaster. In a charge of burglary the evidence of a hundred and forty-nine burglars would not persuade the Court that the prisoner was incapable of house-breaking.

Sir Ethelred: But, your worship . . .

The Chairman: We cannot admit this evidence. The question of obscenity is for the Court to decide.

Sir Ethelred: But, your worship, you have admitted the evidence of the constable.

The Chairman: That is different.

Sir Ethelred : How?

The Chairman : Do not be impertinent, Sir Ethelred. The constable is not a schoolmaster.

Sir Ethelred : Your worship, it is a principle of English law that an accused person is assumed to be innocent until he is proved to be guilty. In this case it appears that the defendant is assumed to be guilty, since he is summoned to show cause why the books in question should not be destroyed; yet he is not permitted to prove himself innocent, for the evidence of ignorant persons is admitted against him and the evidence of educated persons is not admitted in his defence. I protest.

The Bench : Sir Ethelred, you may protest.

Counsel then addressed the Bench. The magistrates withdrew and did not return for several hours.

On their return the Chairman said: This is a very painful case. During our absence we have perused, with growing interest and disgust, a number of passages in the books complained of, and in particular a book called *The Classical Dictionary*, which is written in English. Many of the books are written in a foreign language with which we are not acquainted; some of these are accompanied by English translations, and some are not; but from the character of the former we are entitled to form certain conclusions as to the character of those volumes which no one has yet been bold enough to put into English.

The Classical Dictionary is a book of six hundred and forty pages and contains a very large number of legends or stories concerning so-called classical or mythological figures. I am glad to say that no one on this Bench has had a classical education, and we were therefore able to approach these volumes with an open mind. The magistrates on my right and left include a baker, a brewer, a farmer, and a distinguished banker, and, though none of us are professors or schoolmasters, Sir Ethelred, you will admit, I think, that we are as well able as other men to say what is fit and proper to be read by young persons.

Sir Ethelred : Certainly, your worship.

The Chairman : Now we are informed that the definition of

obscenity laid down by Lord Cockburn in the case of *R.* v. *Hicklin* was as follows: 'I think the test . . . is whether the tendency of the matter charged as obscenity is to deprave and corrupt those whose minds are open to such immoral influences and into whose hands a publication of this sort may fall.' The last words are important. Not only the nature of the work but the circumstances of its publication, including its price, must be taken into account. A treatise on the passion of love, philanthropically intended and decently expressed, might be most unsuitable to be read by young persons, and if it were hawked in the streets for twopence might properly be condemned under the Act, but not if it were sold at a high price by reputable booksellers, in which case it would be most unlikely to fall into the hands of young persons.[1] But in the present case the publications complained of have been deliberately purchased and kept for the consumption of young persons, and young persons drawn exclusively from the aristocracy and the governing classes, whose duty it will be in future years to set an example to their less fortunate countrymen, to mould their minds and dictate their actions. Any conduct therefore which tends to corrupt and deprave those young persons must be held especially culpable.

We find unanimously that these volumes have such a tendency. The legends in *The Classical Dictionary* have a pagan origin and are largely concerned with pagan gods; and their amorous adventures and barbaric standards of behaviour form strange subjects of study for the pupils of a Royal College situated under the walls of a Royal Castle whose august occupant is head of the Established Church. We have read with particular repugnance the record of the alleged god, Zeus, whose habit it was to assume the shape of swans, bulls, and other animals, and, thus disguised, to force his unwelcome attentions upon defenceless females of good character. The case of the woman Leda, if it were published in the newspapers today, would arouse the indignation of every right-

---

1. See *Chief Constable of Burbleton* v. *Woolworth* (1929), in which defendants published a sixpenny edition of the Plays of Shakespeare. The magistrates ordered it to be destroyed.

thinking Englishman; and we have no doubt that our leaders of thought would mobilize the conscience of the nation to prevent the repetition of such offences. But in these books we learn that, although the unfortunate woman became the mother of two eggs, the celestial profligate was permitted to proceed without public protest to the odious case of the woman Europa, in which the abductor took the shape of a bull. No moral reproof is founded on these stories, no improving lesson is drawn from them; on the contrary, they are related with a callous indifference which, coupled with the fact that the delinquent is of a divine or pseudo-divine character, must tend to suggest to the susceptible imagination of the young that such behaviour is defensible or even desirable. The boys of Eton must not be encouraged to dress themselves as swans or wild beasts for the purpose of idle and illicit flirtation; but that can be the only effect of these deplorable anecdotes. Indeed, we learn without surprise that the Captain of the Boats was recently expelled for entering the Matron's bedroom disguised as a brown owl.

I could mention many other passages, only less disgraceful in that they relate the moral lapses of mortal men and not of gods – the case, for example, of the man Oedipus, who killed his own father and married his own mother. Then there is the revolting story of the woman Medea, who committed or was accessory to a number of atrocious murders. This woman, by false representations, induced the daughters of Pelias to cut their father in pieces and boil him; she sent to a female rival a poisoned garment which burned the unfortunate woman to death; she murdered her own brother and herself cut him into fragments; she killed and (according to one account) devoured her own children; but, so far from paying the due penalty of her crimes, she was then conveniently conveyed to safety in a chariot drawn by winged dragons. Strange food, this, for the tender minds of our growing aristocracy. It must not be forgotten that the mind can be 'corrupted and depraved' in more than one direction; tales of parricide, fratricide, and infanticide are 'obscene' in the truest sense of the word; and all through these legends there runs a strain of violence and cruelty and bloodthirsty vengeance which is as harmful to the reader as the strain of irregular passion. It is idle for us to urge upon the newspapers and the makers of films the duty of reticence in their treatment of crimes and offences if our places of education are permitted to discuss them without restraint; and it may well be that the prevalent appetite of the poor for tales of murder and wrongdoing has its real origin in the schools and colleges of the rich.

We have been asked by counsel to take into account the innocent motives of the defendant, the artistic merits of the works in question and the long tradition which has admitted them as proper reading for the young. It was decided in the year 1868 that innocence of motive is no defence to a charge under the Act; and neither art nor custom can, in this Court at least, excuse an offence against morals. We find that these books are corrupting and we order them to be destroyed. Fortunately we have only been called upon to consider a fraction of the so-called 'classics'; but after what we have seen we shall recommend to the proper authorities that a thorough survey be made of the whole body of classical literature in order that our schools and colleges may be made safe for aristocracy. The defendant is severely censured and will pay the costs.[1]

8 January 1930

Note: The passing of the Obscene Publications Act 1959, which repealed Lord Campbell's Act, did not excite universal applause: but at least it should secure our educational institutions against similar assaults.

Under Section 4 ('Defence of Public Good') a person shall not be convicted under Section 2, and an order for forfeiture shall not be made by a magistrate:

if it is proved that publication of the article in question is justified as being for the public good on the ground that it is in the interests of science, literature, art, or learning, or of other objects of general concern.

1. In a later case, *Rex* v. *Squire*, the defendant, a street bookmaker, attributed his downfall to a volume of Catullus which he had picked up in the streets of Windsor.

and the opinion of experts as to the literary, artistic, scientific, or other merits of an 'article' may be admitted in evidence. It should not be difficult to prove that such writers as Homer and Horace have marked literary merit. The 'dead languages' are less studied than they were but they are more and more employed in the language of the people. Every new invention, disease, or remedy is given a Greek or Latin name. 'Radio', the supreme channel of communication, is now divided into 'audio' and 'video'. Then there is the strange term 'discothèque'. The modern witch-doctor, the psychiatrist, can hardly open his mouth without dropping classical words and characters. Whatever posterity may think of the conduct of Zeus and others their languages must be accepted as a branch of 'learning' and its preservation a 'public good'.

The Let and Hindrance

HADDOCK *v*. THE KING; HADDOCK *v*. CONSTABLE
BOOT; HADDOCK *v*. THE SOUTHERN RAILWAY

A DECISION of the highest constitutional importance was
given in this case by the House of Lords today.

The Lord Chancellor : These three appeals have, by leave of
your Lordships, been treated as one appeal. The facts are
quickly stated. The appellant, Mr Albert Haddock, presented
himself at Victoria Station with a railway and boat ticket for
the French port of Calais, issued to him by the Southern Railway. The official at the barrier of the platform inspected the
ticket and requested Mr Haddock to exhibit his passport. Mr
Haddock replied, in direct but courteous terms, that the
Southern Railway had contracted to carry him to Calais, that
it was not a term of that contract that he should exhibit or even
carry a passport, and that he declined to exhibit his passport to
a subordinate official of the Southern Railway, who would be
better employed in making his journey comfortable than in
barring his passage and thus unnecessarily augmenting the
nervous strain incidental to a journey. There was some debate,
but at length the official, either impressed by Mr Haddock's
personality and command of language or preferring to leave the
responsibility of a decision to his colleagues at Dover, permitted him to pass on to the train.

At Dover, when Mr Haddock approached the steam-packet,
the same request was made and was again refused. But here
the official was not to be persuaded, and, although satisfied that
Mr Haddock's ticket was in order, would not allow him to
approach the vessel, but even offered him physical resistance,
amounting technically to an assault. Mr Haddock insisted; the
attention of Constable Boot was attracted; the constable and
the official conferred together; it was decided between them
that Mr Haddock's refusal or inability to exhibit his passport
was a suspicious circumstance suggesting that he was a criminal

fleeing from justice, and Mr Haddock was detained – or, to use the proper term, arrested – for inquiries. Mr Haddock immediately presented his banker's letter of credit and various documents and photographs which established his identity and respectability; but these were not considered sufficient and the vessel proceeded to France without him.

The Southern Railway have attempted to justify their conduct by pleading that they acted as they did under the orders of His Majesty's Secretary of State for Foreign Affairs; and Mr Haddock was ill-advised enough to bring in the first place an action against the Crown for inducing a breach of his contract with the Southern Railway. Here, as the Courts below have successively decided, and as he himself must be very well aware, he has no title of a case. 'The King can do no wrong',[1] and therefore he cannot induce a breach of contract or be liable for any other tortious act. This may seem strange to those students of history who supposed that the despotic privileges of the Crown were surrendered or destroyed in the seventeenth century, but that is the law. In this case, therefore, Mr Haddock's appeal must be dismissed.

But the quaint old rule that the King can do no wrong does not mean that he is entitled to command his subjects to do wrong, or to save them harmless if they obey him. It would not, for example, be a good defence to a charge of murder that the King, through the Foreign Secretary, had expressed a dislike for the murdered man; though the King in his clemency might graciously pardon the murderer *after he had been convicted*. This distinction is important – indeed it is fundamental.

The appellant (who cannot, we think, be quite so guileless as he appears to be) then brought actions against Constable Boot for false imprisonment, and against the Southern Railway for assault (by their servant) and breach of contract. It was urged upon us that the appellant has a bee in his bonnet; but as

---

1. '*Rex non potest peccare*'; but *vide* Strauss's *Life and Times of King John*. A foreign ruling prince cannot be cited as a co-respondent in a divorce-suit in England: *Statham* v. *Statham and the Gaekwar of Baroda* (1912) 'Probate Reports', page 92. The correct form of the maxim, therefore, would seem to be '*Nullus rex potest peccare*'.

Lord Mildew observed in the case of *Merivale* v. *Prout*: 'John Hampden had a bee in his bonnet'; and the presence of a bee in that locality is at least a guarantee against cerebral inertia.[1]

It is admitted by the Crown that the Foreign Office did, and does, issue instructions to the Southern Railway that they are to carry no person to France except such as exhibit a passport satisfactory to the Foreign Office. But the Foreign Office is not entitled to issue an instruction to any subject unless that instruction is authorized by an Act of Parliament or by some still surviving, and indubitably surviving, remnant of the prerogative of the Crown.

In this case there is no such Act of Parliament, and the Crown's advisers have not even pretended to discover one. The Foreign Office issues a somewhat peremptory pamphlet entitled, 'Passport Regulations', in which it is stated that every British subject who leaves these shores 'must' do this or that in relation to passports. But it is nowhere stated on what authority that 'must' is founded. And unless it can be shown that these commands and regulations are made by virtue of the Royal prerogative they have no better juridical sanction than the rules of grammar or the canons of metrical composition.

Is there any such prerogative? Has the Crown today, without the authority of Parliament and in times of peace, a power to forbid the subject to leave the kingdom unless he has the consent of the Foreign Secretary? We find that it has not.

On the contrary, our researches have led us to the singular conclusion that such a power or custom did once exist but has been expressly taken away. In Magna Carta it is clearly provided and promised by the Crown – 'for us and for our heirs for ever' – that:

'All merchants shall have their safe and sure conduct to depart out of England, to tarry in and go through England, as well by land as by water, to buy and sell, without any manner of evil tolls, by the old and rightful customs, except in time of war.'

The power which was wrested from King John by the barons (who also suffered, no doubt, from the presence of bees in their

1. And see Bracton: '*Melior est conditio bombinantis quam moribundi.*'

bonnets) has not been restored to the Crown by any subsequent enactment or decision; and in this old-fashioned House we hold that Magna Carta, except where it has been expressly superseded, is still the law.[1] It would be strange if it were otherwise. The King's Dominions and possessions beyond the seas have been conquered, held, and maintained in prosperity through the readiness of his subjects to leave these shores and venture abroad. And that readiness has been in a large measure the fruit of liberty. In times of peace, for many centuries, it has been the unwavering policy of the King and Parliament to extend to the subject who is willing to travel in foreign parts not merely consent but encouragement and even inducements. And one of these inducements has been the personal passport.

What is the passport? It is a document signed by His Majesty's Secretary of State for Foreign Affairs '*requesting and requiring in the name of his Majesty all those whom it may concern to allow the bearer to pass freely without let or hindrance, and to afford him every assistance and protection of which he may stand in need*'.

Evidence has been given in this case which shows that, even where the subject is in possession of what is called a 'valid' passport and obsequiously exhibits it to all who desire to inspect it, the document is in fact productive of more 'lets and hindrances' than any other circumstance of a journey abroad. But in essence the possession of a passport remains a privilege. For the British subject it may even be a right; but it can never be a duty. The distinction of its origin, the use of His Majesty's name, and the generous enthusiasm of its language, may suggest, and are without doubt intended to suggest, that the bearer is a person especially dear to the Crown and therefore of high moral character. But no man is entitled to argue the converse.

Nevertheless, by the arrogance of the Crown's servants and the weak compliance of the subjects, the character of the passport has been in fact transformed. *What was a privilege has become a duty; what was a talisman has become an instrument of*

1. But see *Rex v. Haddock* (page 36) in which it was *held* (Lugg, J.) that Magna Carta was obsolete.

torture; what was intended to facilitate free movement has become an engine of obstruction.[1] In time of war the Crown has an undoubted prerogative to restrict and regulate the movements of the subject. But, my Lords, we are not at war. We are at peace; and it is desirable that the subject should go about the world as readily and as freely as before. It is said that in recent times the readiness of our citizens to venture abroad has diminished, and we are told that the Dominions Office is making special efforts to induce a greater number to leave this country and seek their fortunes over the seas. These efforts are not wholly successful, and, now that we have heard of the obstacles to travel which have been placed by the Foreign Office in Mr Haddock's path, that does not surprise us. Drake himself, confronted with the same discouragements, might well have degenerated into a stay-at-home.

We were told that these Passport Regulations (so-called) are of assistance in preventing the undesirable alien from entering this country; but this is a somewhat fantastic reason for preventing the respectable Briton from leaving it. We were told that they are of use to the police in the apprehension of escaping criminals. But this has nothing to do with us, with Mr Haddock, or indeed with the Foreign Office. The police must devise some method of apprehending the guilty traveller without obstructing and persecuting the innocent.

We were told, again, that the regulations are made for the convenience of the traveller. We do not believe it. They were made for the preservation, in peacetime, of an autocratic power justified only by a state of war, and for the benefit of the passport officers in this and other countries. But whether or not these defences have been erected in sincerity they have no foundation in law. If it is necessary for the good of the realm

1. See *Petain* v. *Bullock* (1927) 2 A.C. 142, where a Channel swimmer, arriving at Dover, was not permitted to land, having no passport, and was compelled to swim back to France. It was *held* that she could not recover from the landing-officer for medical expenses resulting from the fatigues of the return journey. But Monckton points out (*Key Cases in Private International Law*) that the plaintiff in that case was an alien and was wearing no clothes. *Quaere* – would this decision cover the case of a British subject, properly dressed?

that such restrictions exist, then Parliament must say so in clear and unmistakable terms. Parliament has not said so, and Mr Haddock is entitled to proceed to France without exhibiting his passport to any man in these islands. If the French authorities refuse to admit him without a passport that is his own affair. He had in fact a valid passport on his person, which he judged, and rightly judged, was only of interest to the foreign persons to whom it was addressed. Constable Boot and the Southern Railway have injured the appellant; and they may not shelter behind the instructions of the Foreign Office, for those instructions were *ultra vires*, unconstitutional, against public policy, and an 'evil toll' such as is expressly forbidden by Magna Carta. They must pay the consequences. The damages claimed are not extensive, and I recommend that in addition Mr Haddock receive a grant of five thousand pounds from the Crown in recognition of his public services. There is something to be said for the view that the Passport Office might be indicted as an unlawful conspiracy; but that question we are not called upon to determine.

Lord Lick, Lord Arrowroot, Lord Sweet, and Lord Sheep concurred.

Note: And see a later case, at the Hague, 'Ex Parte Haddock', in *Bardot M.P.* (page 109).

At page 115 Mr Haddock notes the subtle and dangerous alteration in the language of the Crown on different passports that he has held.

In 1945 it was:

This passport is a valuable document . . . It should not be altered in any way or allowed to pass into the possession of any unauthorized person.

Nothing about 'property': the document, evidently, belongs to the holder – and rightly, for he has paid for it.

In 1949 it was:

This passport *remains the property of His Majesty's Government,* and may be withdrawn if the holder ceases to be entitled to the protection of His Majesty's Government.

Thus, without notice, and, so far as I know, explanation, the property in the passport suddenly passed from the citizen to the Crown. But the citizen was still compelled to pay for a document which had ceased to belong to him, and I think, had to pay more. Some may say: 'Fair enough. If you misbehave the Crown may rightly require you to return your passport.' I reply: 'Fair enough. But will the Crown return my money?'

In 1958 the Crown takes another stealthy step to tyranny:

This passport remains the property of Her Majesty's Government, and *may be withdrawn at any time.*

'Thus Freedom narrows slowly down . . .' The new formula must mean that a policeman can come to my door, *at any time*, and say: 'I want your passport', without giving any particular reason – and without returning my 30s. This formula abandons the last elements of that gracious favour which was the origin of the passport. It reduces the citizen to the level of a ticket-of-leave man. Further, it exposes him to the worst excesses of foreign bureaucracy. While his passport was his own, he could say at the Spanish hotel: 'No, this is *my* passport, I will *not* have it sent to the police' – or at the frontier: 'This is *my* passport – and you are not to cover it with superfluous and meaningless stamps. Have a look – but give it back to me intact.' He can't say that if it belongs to the Foreign Office.

Is this a Police State?

The Egg of Exchange

HOUSE OF COMMONS (KITCHEN COMMITTEE) *v.*
HADDOCK

(*Before Mr Justice Codd*)

SIR RONALD RUTT, K.C.,[1] opening the case for the plaintiffs
today, said:

May it please your lordship, I appear for the Kitchen
Committee of the House of Commons. As defendant, the
Court, no doubt, will be glad to see that veteran litigant, Mr
Albert Haddock, who is always welcome, however erroneous.
His present appearance arises out of a gathering of dramatists
at the House of Commons, some of whom were Members and
some, more fortunate, were not. Mr Haddock had made himself
responsible for the cost of the refreshments provided, which,
considering the eminence in their profession of many of the
guests, could hardly be described as 'lavish'. Nowadays, if two
citizens occupy a dwelling-place consisting of two small rooms
and a bathroom where some of the appliances work it is described as a 'luxury' flat. But that word, I am satisfied, is not
here appropriate.

At the close of the proceedings, when the bill was presented
to him, Mr Haddock drew a cheque for ten pounds (£10) on
an egg.

The Court: An egg?

Sir Ronald: If your lordship pleases – an egg.

The Court: A turkey's egg?

Sir Ronald: No, milord, a hen's egg. Milord, it appears that
the defendant, no doubt legitimately,[2] had acquired three eggs,
and brought them to the dinner at the House of Commons.

The Court: And the Kitchen Committee are insulted? I do
not wonder. But is this a libel action?

1. Son of Sir Ethelred (now Lord Justice) Rutt.
2. Eggs were fiercely rationed in those days.

Sir Ronald: No, milord. The eggs, it appears, were intended as a tribute to the distinguished dramatist who presided over the gathering.[1] On two of them those present wrote their 'autographs', and these two were duly presented to the President. On the third . . .

The Court: What a party!

Sir Ronald: Your lordship will realize that the company included a good many bright and imaginative spirits. On the third egg, then, in small but legible characters, the defendant drew a cheque for the bill in the ordinary form of words: a stamp was attached and cancelled, according to the Stamp Act, and the whole document, if it can be so described, was presented to the Manager, Major Sidwell, in discharge of the debt. The Manager presented the cheque at the bank having charge of the Kitchen Committee's account, and asked that bank (which I will call Bank B) to collect the money in the usual manner from the defendant's bank (which I will call Bank A). The manager of Bank B, however, demurred to handling the cheque at all, and especially to making himself responsible for forwarding it through the usual channels. It would require, he said, the employment of special receptacles and messengers . . .

The Court: Was the cheque hard-boiled?

Sir Ronald: No, milord, it was a fresh cheque. Indeed, there is some evidence that it was a new-laid cheque.

The Court: What a waste!

Sir Ronald: That, milord, was one of the considerations which affected the minds of my clients. 'No man,' as Lord Mildew said in a recent case, 'can pretend to full cognisance and understanding of all the rules and regulations concerning the feeding of the King's subjects at the present time.' But it would be unlikely, my clients thought, if there were not some Statutory Rule or Order against the use of a fresh egg as a Bill of Exchange.

The Court: Yes, Sir Ronald, but I thought that in these affairs the House of Commons could do what it liked? Surely, that was all settled by the singular but satisfactory case of *Rex*

1. Major Ian Hay Beith.

v. *Sir R. F. Graham-Campbell and others. Ex parte Herbert (1935) 1 K.B.*[1]

Sir Ronald : That is the best opinion, milord: but the House has never cared to abuse its privileges, or to set an unworthy example to the people. If it were to get about, they thought, that Members of the House of Commons were in the habit of using fresh eggs as cheques, promissory notes, I.O.Us. or — who knows? — for the transfer of shares or securities, an unfavourable impression might be made upon a people still bravely suffering under the reign of Austerity.

The Court : But stop a moment, Sir Ronald. I think, perhaps, I was a little hasty. Let us see what would happen to the egg. It was, I take it, the defendant's property? There is no suggestion that it was a pilfered or unrationed egg?

Sir Ronald : No, milord. Indeed, in these days the relevant eggs might even have been what are described officially as 'surplus eggs', though they have still, for most of us, a merely notional existence.

The Court : Pretty notional, I agree, Sir Ronald. Very well. The egg, I suppose, passes from your client's bank, through the Bankers' Clearing House, or whatever it is, to the defendant's bank. They read and obey the instructions on the cheque: and, their duty discharged, return the cheque, as usual, to the defendant. If it were a paper cheque he could use it to light his pipe: if it is an egg cheque, he can eat, or, I suppose I should say, consume it. I do not really see what objections can be raised by the Ministry of Food to such a transaction.

Sir Ronald : As your Lordship pleases. But there remains the question of the difficulties of transit . . .

The Court : Why didn't your bank have the cheque hard-boiled?

Sir Ronald : Milord, that was considered by the bank. But it

1. Here a Divisional Court consisting of Lord Hewart, L. C. J., Mr Justice Avory and Mr Justice Rigby Swift *held*, as a matter of privilege, that the House of Commons were entitled to sell 'drink' without a licence, for the Licensing Acts were not 'applicable'. 'All the privileges that can be required for the energetic discharge of the duties inherent in that high trust are conceded without a murmur or a doubt.' (*Stockdale* v. *Hansard*.)

was thought that the stamp would become detached in the process of boiling, and perhaps the writing be extinguished.

The Court: The stamp, Sir Ronald, could surely have been attached again: and there is nothing, I think, to prevent the holder from attaching and cancelling a new stamp, if necessary. As for the writing, if I know anything of Mr Haddock, he uses one of those queer new pens which write underwater.

Sir Ronald: As to that, milord, I am not instructed.

The Court: Extraordinary. Go on, Sir Ronald.

Sir Ronald: My clients, milord, declined to accept the cheque in payment and presented their account again. The defendant . . .

The Court: The defendant, I suppose, took umbrage? He said that he was not accustomed to having his cheques scorned and rejected – and you could take it or leave it?

Sir Ronald: That was roughly his position, milord. And he has obstinately refused to discharge the debt.

The Court: Sir Ronald, before you proceed any further you may care to consult with your clients, and with learned counsel on the other side. It is true that your clients are not bound to accept a cheque of any kind. But in practice, without doubt, many of your debts are collected in this way; and, having regard to the general custom and his own position, the defendant is naturally reluctant to get the name of one who passes worthless cheques. Your clients, or rather your clients' bank, are not in fact objecting to payment by cheque, but to payment by this particular cheque: and the defendant may well have expected to hear some stronger objections than those which you have, so far, exposed. There is nothing magical or mystical about a cheque. It is simply a written instruction by one person to a second person to pay money to a third – to which, of course, a rapacious State insists upon the addition of a stamp. It does not matter where it is written, provided the intention is clear. It can be written on a bill of fare, upon a napkin, or, if no other paper be available, the label of a brandy-bottle, and such cheques have, in fact, passed safely through the banking channels and been duly honoured and met. It could, I suppose, be written on an out-house or the side of a balloon, provided that it was brought effectively to the notice of the bank addressed and the necessary stamp was attached before presentation. Between a brandy-bottle, an out-house and an egg there can clearly be no great distinction of principle.[1] Nor am I much impressed by the practical difficulties to which you have referred. It is the duty of a bank to keep the stream of commerce flowing and navigable, and to destroy, not to create, new obstacles in the fairway. You tell me, Sir Ronald, that your bank, because of the brittle and breakable quality of the cheque in question, was reluctant to undertake the responsibility of transporting it to the proper quarter, though all that was necessary, after all, was to place the cheque in the hand of a trustworthy boy (or even girl) and hire a motor-cab. On the other hand, it shrank, I understand, from making the simple experiment of boiling the cheque – and boiling it hard. This, Sir Ronald, was not the spirit of those old merchant venturers who made the name of commercial England famous and admired. Of course, if it became a general practice for men of commerce and industry to employ the egg for such purposes, a state of affairs might arise in which Parliament would feel itself compelled to intervene. But it is always a great mistake to treat the individual on the chance that he may become a crowd. And meanwhile, I, at least, have to deal with the law as it stands today. Call Mr Haddock.

Sir Ronald : But, milord . . .!

The Court : I am well aware that this procedure is unusual, Sir Ronald. So is the case.

Mr Albert Haddock was sworn and said: Yesterday I wrote in ordinary ink upon an egg the same form of words as were on the egg in this case. I boiled the egg for nine minutes, and the writing was as clear as ever.

The Court : You see, Sir Ronald? The Court will adjourn.

16 February 1949

Note : The later history of this cheque is recorded in Mabane on *Bills of Exchange*. The cheque was hard-boiled by Major Sidwell,

---

1. See the Negotiable Cow, *Uncommon Law*, page 201.

conveyed to the defendant's bank, Messrs Grindlay's Bank Limited, and duly honoured. It is now in the Museum of Queer Cheques at that establishment, cheques drawn on napkins, the labels of brandy-bottles, bills of fare, etc., cheques drawn in verse and uncomplimentary language, cheques illustrated with sketches for the better identification of the drawer and drawee, etc. 'They are all my property,' said Mr Haddock laughingly in a recent interview, 'and should have been returned to me. But my good Bank has impounded them. Never mind. They have my overdraft too.'

Blackmail

REX v. PUDDLE

THE Hammersmith Blackmail Case was concluded at the Old Bailey today.

Mr Justice Trout (addressing the jury) : Gentlemen, this is a very grave case. The prisoner in the dock, a Collector of Taxes for the district of South Hammersmith, stands charged with the odious crime which is commonly described as blackmail. That expression dates from very early times, when it was the custom to pay tribute to men of influence who were allied with certain robbers and brigands for protection from the devastations of the latter. The practice was made illegal by a statute of Queen Elizabeth's time, and ever since it has been classed by our Courts among the most contemptible and dangerous offences. A person, who, knowing the contents, sends or delivers a letter or writing *demanding with menaces and without reasonable cause* any chattel, money, or other property, commits felony, and is liable to penal servitude for life. The menace, the 'putting in fear', as our ancestors expressed it, is of the essence of the crime. The spectacle of one man demanding money from another must always be painful to the civilized mind; but when in addition that other is made to fear for his safety, liberty, or reputation the law steps in to protect and punish.

Now, Mr Haddock, the prosecutor in this case, received a letter from the prisoner demanding money. The letter was printed in ink of a bright red colour, and that is a circumstance which you may well take into account when you come to consider the intention of the letter and the effect which it may have had upon the mind of the recipient. For red is notoriously the colour of menace, of strife, of bloodshed and danger; and it is worthy of note that the prisoner's previous communications to Mr Haddock had been printed in a quiet and pacific blue. The letter was as follows:

Previous applications for payment of the taxes due from you on the 1st day of January, 1930, for the year 1929–30, having been made to you without effect, DEMAND is now made for payment, and I HEREBY GIVE YOU FINAL NOTICE that if the amount be not paid or remitted to me at the above address within SEVEN DAYS from this date steps will be taken for recovery by DISTRAINT, with costs.

E. PUDDLE, Collector

'Collector', I may observe in passing, was in other centuries a word commonly used to denote a highwayman.[1] But you will not allow that point to influence you unduly.

Now the 'demand' is clear; indeed the word, as you will notice, is printed in block capitals. And you have to say, first of all, whether or not that 'demand' is accompanied by menaces. You will take everything into consideration, the terseness, I almost said the brutality, of the language, the intimidating red ink, the picking out in formidable capitals of the words 'DEMAND', 'SEVEN DAYS', and 'DISTRAINT', and any other circumstance which may seem to you calculated to cause alarm in the mind of the recipient. You will observe in particular the concluding words, 'Steps will be taken for recovery by DISTRAINT, with costs.'

'DISTRAINT.' What is the exact meaning of that? It means the forcible seizure of a person's goods; it means the invasion of his home by strangers; it amounts to licensed burglary; it means the loss not only of favourite possessions but of reputation; it means distress to wife and family, and it is significant that the correct and common term for the process is 'Distress'. Evidence has been given that a threat 'to put the bailiffs in' brings terror to any home. The prosecutor has sworn that at

1. In *Rex* v. *Strauss* (1928) 9 Cr. App., R. 91, a bailiff acting for the Inland Revenue was struck and killed with a book of sermons while removing a wireless set belonging to the accused, and two rabbits, the property of a favourite daughter. The defence was that distress for income tax was a gross provocation comparable to the discovery of a wife in the arms of another (see *Rex* v. *Maddy*, 1 Ventris, 158), and such as to produce an uncontrollable impulse depriving a man of the ordinary powers of self-control. The jury, without leaving the box, returned a verdict of 'Justifiable Homicide', but the following day was Derby Day, and the decision is not regarded as settled law.

the sight of that one red word he suffered alarm; that he understood from the letter that, without opportunity to state his case in a court of law, his goods would be seized and his wife and family put in fear by the prisoner. The prisoner says that that was not his intention; that the words 'steps will be taken for recovery' indicated a preliminary summons to the Court. You may think that in that case he would have done better to print those words in the same large type as the word 'DISTRAINT'; and you may think, as I do, looking at all the circumstances, that the letter was deliberately planned and worded with the intention of creating alarm, and, through that alarm, extracting money from Mr Haddock, who is a sensitive man.

You will then have to ask yourselves, Was this menacing demand for money made with reasonable cause? You will bear in mind that Mr Haddock is not a debtor or a criminal; he has not taken another's property or done any disgraceful thing. His only offence is that by hard work he has earned a little money; and the suggestion is now made that he shall give away a fourth part of that money to other people. That being his position, you might well expect that he would be approached not with brusquerie but with signal honours, not with printed threats but with illuminated addresses. But the whole tenor of the prisoner's communications suggests that in his opinion Mr Haddock is a guilty person. Observe the strange use of the word 'recovery' – as if Mr Haddock had *taken* money from the prisoner. Mr Haddock has made repeated protests to the Collector and to his confederate, the Inspector, urging that even under the strange customs of our land the sum demanded of him was excessive, that due allowance had not been made for the particular hardships and expenses of his professional calling, and that in his judgment the prisoner and his principals have taken from him during the past years money which they ought in conscience to restore. While this dispute was still proceeding the prisoner sent this letter. Mr Haddock, a public-spirited man, conveyed the letter to the police, and it is for you to say whether he was right. An official from the Inland Revenue Department has drawn your attention to the difficulties of a Mr Snowden, the prisoner's principal, it appears, who is in need of money. You will pay no attention to that. We are all in need of money; and if Mr Snowden[1] has an insufficient supply of money he must spend less money, as the rest of us have to do. Neither his avarice nor his extravagance can excuse a breach of the law.

The jury eagerly found the prisoner guilty of blackmail, and he was sentenced to penal servitude for life, and solitary confinement for ten years, the sentences to run consecutively. The Court congratulated Mr Haddock.

2 April 1930

Note: And see, in *Bardot M.P.*, page 57, 'The Bottle Case', where the defendant, during a transport strike, committed his payment, with due warning, to the Thames at Hammersmith, and the Inland Revenue were *held* guilty of negligence in failing to 'collect' it.

1. Philip Snowden, then Chancellor of the Exchequer.

Port to Port

RUMPELHAMMER *v.* HADDOCK

THIS case, involving some difficult points of Marine and Traffic Law, was brought to a conclusion today.

The President of the Probate, Divorce, and Admiralty Division (who had the assistance of an assessor) giving judgment, said:

This action was originally instituted in the King's Bench; but, Mr Justice Juice holding that the issues disclosed pertained to the Law of Admiralty, although the ground of the claim was damage to a motor-car, the case was withdrawn from the King's Bench List and referred to this Court.

Mr Rumpelhammer is suing Mr Haddock for negligent behaviour on the highroad, as a result of which his motor-car, a costly Botellini-Nine, was damaged. The dispute, as is usual at the present time, is only nominally between the parties named, the real litigants being two insurance companies. If it were not for the insurance companies there would be very little litigation of any kind today, and members of the legal profession owe to them a debt which we can only repay by careful labour and clear decisions.

On the 21st March last Mr Rumpelhammer was driving his motor-car along the thoroughfare known as Chiswick Mall, which runs beside the north bank of the River Thames. Now, it appears that during the high spring tides, particularly those of the equinoctial seasons, the waters of the Thames overflow the banks and cover the highway to a depth of from two feet on the river side of the road to a few inches on the landward side. Such was the condition of affairs a little before high water on the date in question, when Mr Rumpelhammer, who had an important business appointment in the City, began his voyage along the Mall. His evidence is that he was keeping carefully to the left or landward side of the road, where it was still possible to drive through the shallow water without fear of damage. While thus engaged he was startled, he says, to see ahead of

him, and coming towards him on the same side of the road, the
defendant, Mr Haddock, who was navigating with a paddle a
small boat of shallow draught. The plaintiff blew his horn
vigorously, but the defendant held his course. Mr Rumpelhammer shouted courteously, 'Out of the road, you fool!' and
Mr Haddock replied, as he admitted under cross-examination,
'Port to port, you foxy beetle! Are you not acquainted with the
Regulations for Preventing Collisions at Sea? I am going to
starboard.'

The plaintiff judged from this speech that he had to do with a
maniac, and, obeying an instinct of humanity which in the
circumstances deserves all praise, he swerved to the right rather
than collide with the defendant's flimsy craft. But this man-
oeuvre brought him into the deeper water, which penetrated
to the delicate mechanism of his motor and caused it to stop.

It would not be profitable or seemly to dwell upon the
exchange of views which followed. Although clearly expressed
they reflect small credit on the breeding and education of either
party. Mr Rumpelhammer was compelled to remain where he
was until the tide fell. (Mr Haddock, by the way, in gross
breach of the customs of the sea, declined to convey him to the
shore or pavement in his boat, on the ground that he feared a
breach of the peace.) On the waters subsiding it was found that
the car had been seriously damaged, and it had to be towed to
the nearest garage. Mr Rumpelhammer was unable to keep his
appointment, and as a result, he tells us, suffered pecuniary
loss.

The evidence of Mr Haddock was most unsatisfactory, and
if he thought that by singing snatches of sea-shanties he would
commend himself to the Admiralty Court he was mistaken.
Further, he has imported into the case a deplorable element
of personal prejudice. He made certain comments on the personal appearance of the plaintiff which he must have known
can have no juridical significance. He said that he had once or
twice with resentment observed the defendant going about the
neighbourhood in an opulent motor-car of foreign make, driving
to the public danger, in excess of the statutory speed-limit, and
to his (Mr Haddock's) inconvenience and alarm. He said the

plaintiff seemed to think that he might be a law unto himself on the highroads, but that he (Mr Haddock) was blowed if he (Mr Rumpelhammer) was going to get away with it on the high seas as well. He had therefore acted as he did, willing to discomfit Mr Rumpelhammer, but believing that the law was on his side, that is to say, the regulations for the prevention of collisions at sea or in tidal waters.

The defendant is clearly one who insufficiently appreciates the value of the motor-car to the human race. But we must not allow our natural detestation for such an individual to cloud our judgment. The meanest citizen, impelled by the meanest motives, is entitled to insist upon the enforcement of the law. The question is, 'What is the law?' – a question which frequently arises in our Courts and sometimes receives a satisfactory answer.

Now, the law or custom of the road is that when two vehicles meet each shall keep to the left. But the law or custom of the sea is that when two vessels meet they shall go to starboard and pass port to port, that is to say, each shall keep to the right. It is the contention of Mr Haddock that when the tide covers the road that road becomes a part of the tideway, that traffic upon it is thenceforth governed by the regulations and customs of the sea, and that he did right, therefore, to steer so as to pass Mr Rumpelhammer on his port hand. Further, it is the duty of a steam-vessel to keep out of the way of a rowing-boat; and Mr Haddock argues that the plaintiff's motor-car when navigating the tideway has the status of a steam-vessel, and that plaintiff has nobody but himself to blame.

With considerable reluctance we find that there is some substance in these contentions. The law of the land says one thing; the law of the water says the contrary; and it seems elementary that (upon navigable waters) the law of the water must prevail. It is idle to say that Chiswick Mall was not at the time of the accident navigable water. Mr Haddock was, in fact, navigating it, and if Mr Rumpelhammer chooses to navigate it at the same time he must be bound by the appropriate regulations and should make himself familiar with them. Mr Rumpelhammer makes the rather childish objection that his motor-car is not a vessel and ought not to be treated as such. I find no difficulty there. Recent developments of the internal-combustion engine, and in particular the outboard motor, have produced a type of water-conveyance which in aspect and dignity is little more than a floating automobile; and though Mr Rumpelhammer's motor-car appears to be unseaworthy it is otherwise as much a boat as many motor-boats. The point is that, boat or not, it was navigating the tideway.

Again, it was argued for the plaintiff that, since the highroad was only covered with water by an exceptional inundation of short duration, it cannot be held to have lost the character of a highroad. But to accept this view would be to admit a very dangerous and confusing precedent. Suppose that large sections of our southern counties were covered for a long period by exceptional floods, so that the inhabitants were compelled to cross them regularly in steam- or motor-vessels, can it be doubted that the regulations of the water, as to the avoidance of collisions, the carrying of lights, sound signals in case of fog, and so forth, would be observed and enforced in that area? Yet in principle the two cases are the same; and differences of degree cannot be allowed to derogate from principle. The fact that a certain area of water was once dry land and is expected to be dry land again is unimportant. Much of what we now know as land was once covered by the ocean, and vice versa; but a motorist would not be allowed to appeal to the customs of the sea because he was crossing the Romney Marshes, on the ground that that land used to be sea. In the same way it is idle for the plaintiff to urge that Chiswick Mall used to be dry land. The question in every case must be a question of fact – Was this area at the material date water or dry land? And neither geographical size nor extent of time is a relevant consideration. We find in this case that the scene of the mishap was water, and tidal water. Now, tidal waters lead to the ocean and are navigated by the vessels of every maritime country. The regulations upon which Mr Haddock relies are not of British origin or sanction only; they govern the movements and secure the safety of the ships of the world. The nations rely upon each other to observe them faithfully and defend them jealously.

It will be easily seen what international complications might ensue if it were to go forth that the Admiralty Court of Great Britain was prepared to play fast and loose with them for the benefit of a motorist, however small the issues at stake. The defendant is no gentleman, but that is neither here nor there. We find for the defendant, much as we dislike him.

2 July 1930

Note: See Bracton: '*Lex non risu deletur*' or 'Ridicule will not repeal', or (Lord Mildew in *The Dukeries Case*): 'A man may laugh at the law, but the law will laugh last.' See *Rex* v. *Flanagan* (1919) 2 A.C., in which the wife of a plumber died intestate leaving issue three children and net personalty £31,482. A charge of murder was preferred against the plumber, who raised the defence that, man and wife being at Common Law one person, it could not be murder to kill his wife. The plea was allowed, and a verdict of 'Suicide while of unsound mind' was returned; but it was *held* (Mould, J.L., dissenting) that, being insane, the man was ineligible for unemployment relief. See also *Earl of Erne* v. *Maltravers and Gareth* (1893, 2 H.L.), where the Yaffle hounds hunted an aged peer for four miles over the property of the plaintiff, who had forbidden the Hunt to cross his boundaries. In an action for trespass it was *held* (Fruit, L.J., dissenting) that though the Master had been guilty of negligence in employing short-sighted foxhounds, their pursuit of Lord Gareth was an Act of God which he could not have foreseen or prevented. On appeal, however, the House of Lords decided that, though not responsible for damage done by the dogs, he must make good that which was due to the passage of himself and his horse, and the case was referred to assessors for apportionment *quantum pertinet*. Later, on a writ of *quo corpore* (*Rex* v. *Maltravers*), the Master was found guilty of constructive assault in venery, and went bankrupt. (And see Wedderburn on *Water-courses*.)

The Decree Nisi

PIPP, M. L., *v.* PIPP, K., AND FORREST

MR JUSTICE WOOL, who, owing to illness, is doing duty in the Divorce Court, astonished legal circles by a characteristic judgment in this case today. At the close of the learned arguments he said:

In this case there is no doubt that the Court ought to decree that the marriage of Mr and Mrs Pipp be dissolved on the petition of the wife; and so I do decree. But, unfamiliar as I am with this Court, I learn with some surprise that, according to statute, this decree will not take effect for six months from the present date. It is a decree *nisi* – or 'unless'. In other words, I am to say: 'The Court thinks that this marriage ought to be dissolved, *unless* within six months the Court finds that it has made a mistake.' Gosh! Sir Ethelred, what a thing for a British Court to say!

We have here surely one of the strangest provisions in the Statute Book, which is a vast jungle of strange and primitive things. In the first place, it offends my dignity and, I think, the dignity of British justice, for it is a confession of failure. I am accustomed on the Bench to make up my mind once and for all. I hear the evidence, I study the witnesses, I judge to the best of my ability whether they are speaking the truth or not; I listen to learned counsel, and then I decide. I decide that, in my judgement, for what it is worth, A's case is a good one and B's is not. I am prepared to be reversed upon appeal by judges of greater learning and ability; but I am not prepared to reverse myself a few months later an opinion at which I have arrived with so much trouble and thought. I am not prepared to say to a plaintiff, 'Yes, you are quite right; your partner in business has done the dirty on you, and the partnership should be dissolved. But don't be surprised if in six months' time I say, "Yah! I never meant it! The partnership must be kept in being."' For this appears to be the utterance of an imbecile or an infant; and I never was asked to say such a thing before.

What is the ground of this lunatic arrangement? It is that Mrs Pipp may not be telling the whole truth; that there may have been collusion and so forth; and that in the interval the King's Proctor may go procking about and find that in some material particular the Court is being deceived. But if the Court is being deceived we ought to discover it here and now; and if it is necessary for the Proctor to prock about in people's private lives he should do it before the case comes into Court, not after.

I do not myself think that any such procking is either desirable or decent. This Court is equipped with all the elaborate and expensive apparatus for the discovery of truth that centuries of experience have made available, with learned judges and learned counsel, the rules of evidence, the sanctity of the Oath, and the penalties for contempt and perjury. And if that apparatus is to be relied upon elsewhere I see no reason for distrusting it here. In no other department of justice is it thought necessary to employ a sort of extra-judicial spy whose business it is to peep through the keyholes of litigants and find out that His Majesty's judges are being deceived. If it is a good thing in divorce suits it must be a good thing in libel actions, in insurance and running-down cases, or actions for fraud. In every case the parties may say one thing in Court and another in their homes and offices. But the Court in every other case relies upon its own powers to catch the liars out.

I think myself that the methods of the King's Proctor are least of all desirable in cases relating to marriage, where the private lives and affections of the citizen are the subject of investigation. But I had better not say what I think about the whole business of prockery or those prigs in the House of Commons will reduce my salary again.

So much, then, for the dignity of the Court. The thought that in six months from now the King's Proctor may come prancing into this Court and say to me, 'Ha! ha! old man, you were wrong! You thought that Mrs Pipp was an honest woman, but she was lying all the time!' is inexpressibly repugnant to me. But I am thinking also, in humane fashion, of the sufferings of Mrs Pipp. Consider her position. It is idle to say that six months is but a short time to wait: though for those who are more happily situated it is an easy thing to say. Time, as we know, must be measured in relative terms. Six months is not a short time to a soldier in the trenches or to a lonely man upon a desert island. It will not be a short time to Mrs Pipp. Three years have passed already since her husband left her, and seven months since the petition was filed. She is young, lively, and attractive, and I have no doubt that there is some young gentleman who wishes to marry her. But for the next six months she must be in effect a lonely woman on a desert island. I tell her that she is to be free, but for six months she is free upon probation only. She knows that the King's Proctor is at her heels, scrutinizing not only her past but her present behaviour. She knows that a single foolish step may cost her her freedom. She knows that anyone who cares to write an anonymous letter, though it may be malicious and untrue, may bring more trouble upon her. She will hardly dare to speak to any man and must shun entirely the one man in the world for whose company she hungers. Every time she draws a blind she will look for a watcher outside, and every time she retires for the night she will look, if she is wise, for the King's Proctor under the bed. She will be advised by her solicitor, I am told, that it is dangerous for her to return home later than half-past ten or eleven at night. For six months she will feel herself a marked woman, a hunted woman, a woman who is neither wife, widow, nor spinster, bound by particular curfews and codes of conduct – a thing apart from the common run of humanity.

All this might be well enough, by way of penalty, if she were the guilty party; but she is not. And while this innocent woman is followed from place to place by the King's Proctor's agents and her own nervous fears, the guilty husband and his paramour may do what they will. Is it really to be said that in these conditions six months is but a short time to wait?

It is not. And I do not see why Mrs Pipp, after all that she has suffered, should be sentenced to a further six months of humiliating and mournful suspense through the inability of the law to make up its mind. Sir Ethelred Rutt has kindly explained to me the real foundation of the whole queer business. It is that the English law of divorce, by its insanity, encourages lying. Every one who comes into this Court is presumed to be lying until the contrary is shown; and therefore we have a special officer and a special period for the detection of any liars who may escape on the first examination. In Scotland the law encourages the parties to tell the truth, so that there is no King's Proctor and no six months' suspense. In short, the laws of Scotland are civilized and sound, but the laws of England are barbarous. On that large subject, however, I will say no more for the present. I have heard Mrs Pipp cross-examined; I have watched her carefully and believe her to be honest. I therefore this morning grant her a decree of dissolution *nisi*, but this is to be antedated by six months, that is, with the appropriate date in February last; and after lunch I shall make the decree absolute. (*Loud cheers in court*)

Thanks, one and all. What's the next bit of nonsense, please?

2 August 1933

Note: On this subject the English authorities have never been able to make up their minds so firmly as the Scots, or Mr Justice Wool. Under the original Matrimonial Causes Act 1857 a decree was final: an Act of 1860 instituted the decree *nisi*. The interval was three months, but it was extended to six months in 1866. In his Marriage Bill 1937 your editor sought to abolish the *nisi*, but, on very high advice, the clause had to be withdrawn. Since 1925 the Court has had power 'by general or special order' to fix a shorter period 'from time to time'. Judges, in special cases, e.g. to avoid illegitimacy, often gave facilities for expediting the decree absolute, 'with the leave of the King's Proctor'. No 'general order' was made till 1946 when there was a startling reduction to six weeks. In 1957 it was increased to three months.

Such strange things happen in this neck of the woods that we should not be too unkind to the authorities. In a 1966 case a man divorced his wife, in the 'undefended' list, but, through the negligence of solicitors, his wife knew nothing about it. Stranger still, he went on living with her, regarding her now as his 'housekeeper', but not bothering to inform her of her change in status until an accident compelled him. Both the decree *nisi* and decree absolute were then rescinded, and the judge put the case in the defended list, with the wife as plaintiff. But suppose the odd fellow, quite lawfully, had married somebody else?

The Whale Case

HADDOCK *v.* OUNDLE; HADDOCK *v.* SMITH;
HADDOCK *v.* THE GENERAL PRESS; HADDOCK
v. BUZZINGS AND THE BILIOUS WEEKLY;
HADDOCK *v.* COOPER

MR JUSTICE RATCHET, giving judgment today in the '*De mortuis*' case, said:

In this unusual series of actions, which for the general convenience have been heard together, the plaintiff, Mr Albert Haddock, is suing a number of persons and papers for libel. Mr Haddock, while a passenger in a small sailing-vessel which was proceeding southward along the coast of Labrador, had the misfortune to fall overboard. What is now known as 'fog conditions', but the Court still prefers to describe simply as fog, prevailed. The crew did what they could, but were unable to pick up the plaintiff. On that coast at that time of the year are many large icebergs, and in the sub-Arctic water no swimmer could be expected to survive for long.

Accordingly, on the return of the vessel to Newfoundland, the captain sorrowfully reported that the plaintiff must be presumed to have perished in the icy sea. The distressing news was telegraphed to London: obituary notices of the plaintiff's life and professional career appeared in many organs of opinion; and there was a fairly well-attended memorial service at St Luke's, Brunswick Square.

But a few days later news came to this country that the plaintiff was still alive. Besides icebergs, there are numerous whales in those waters: and, according to the plaintiff's story, which he has repeated in the box with a wealth of plausible detail, he was, like the prophet Jonah, swallowed by a whale. He contrasted vividly the warm interior of the mammal with the freezing grip of the ocean. He repelled, under cross-examination, the suggestion that the whale, being fitted with a trellis-like or 'grid-iron' structure in its mouth for the purpose of catching small fish, is quite incapable of swallowing a man – or perhaps I should now say, adult male person. Not all whales, the plaintiff assured the court, are thus constructed,[1] and, if they were, what would become of the story of the prophet Jonah, which has never yet been doubted – except, maybe, by the prophet's wife on his return. We do not know what she said. We do not know what was said by the wife of Sir Isaac Newton when he informed her that after observing the fall of an apple he had solved the riddle of the spheres. We do not know what comment was made by the wife of William Shakespeare when he announced that he proposed to establish the family fortunes by writing a stage-play called *Henry IV*, Part One. Fortunately, the Court is not required to arrive at a finding of fact upon these points: but it is useful to recall that many stories as unlikely as the plaintiff's have been accepted without a murmur for many centuries. He said, by the way, that the whale was a white whale; and he asserted that in those regions more white whales were encountered than black.[2] When asked if that did not make nonsense of *Moby Dick*, that masterpiece of literature, he answered that that was no affair of his.

Next day, the narrative continued, the whale in question was harpooned by the whaling-ship *Terra Nova* and towed into the whaling-station at Hawkes Bay, Labrador. The carcass was at once cut up, and – fortunately before the boiling process – the plaintiff was extracted, not much the worse.

Whatever may be thought of this story, which received keen attention throughout the world, there is no doubt that the plaintiff is alive, and indeed is present in court. The defendants' counsel, unwilling to accept the episode of the whale, has suggested that in fact he was picked up by the fishing schooner *Heart of Grace*, which brought him to Newfoundland:

1. See *Physeter catodon* (sperm whale): 'size gigantic . . . head immense . . . snout enormous' (*Encyclopaedia Britannica*, Vol. 5, p. 171*b*).

2. See *Independent Member*, by A. P. Herbert (Methuen & Co.), 25s. (absurdly cheap), p. 284: 'I asked the Norwegian (manager) if they ever saw a white whale. He said that they catch many white whales.'

and this contention, right or wrong, has more relevance than may at first appear to the issue joined before the Court. On his return to England the plaintiff took exception to certain expressions in some of his 'obituary notices'. Death comes unexpected to most men still: and insufficient praise is given to those great newspapers which produce so readily the following morning a careful account and assessment of the careers of public men; though the thought that in so many offices the record is being ghoulishly brought up to date each year in readiness for the last event must be disturbing to anyone in the public eye. The ancient motto *De mortuis* still seems to prevail in these accounts. The plaintiff does not claim that any of his 'obituaries' was deliberately offensive, though he was disappointed by them all. They were not even likely to aggravate the grief of his relatives if he had been dead. But they are, he says, of a character to damage him in his profession now that he is, in fact, alive. In particular, he objected to the suggestion that, though a careful observer and recorder, he was lacking in imagination. Two writers, he complains, hinted that he was a seeker after publicity, though in fact he is the shyest man alive and suffers a sharp physical revulsion when he sees his name in the papers. Why such a charge should be pressed or resented in the case of a writer is not clear to the Court; for if his name is not known to many how can many be expected to buy his books? It would be as reasonable to blame a nun for her retiring ways. But to say that a romantic author has no imagination may well be damaging, all must agree: and the same, perhaps, applies to Mr Oundle's observation that the plaintiff was deficient in a sense of the sublime.

Now, it is established law that a libel suit cannot be entertained which arises out of anything written concerning a dead person. Other remedies must be sought by the aggrieved family where the dead are defamed. The defendants say that in good faith and upon proper information they presumed the plaintiff to be dead; that what they published was published only on that assumption and would not have been published had they known him to be alive; that any reasonable man would have thought him to be dead; that at the time of publication he was constructively dead; that the libel, if any, was a libel, to all intents and purposes, on a dead man, and therefore cannot be a cause of action.

This argument, though it was pressed with much ingenuity and force by Sir Ambrose Wett, the Court is unable to accept. We find that the plaintiff was in fact alive when the words complained of were published; and the fact that he was in the belly of a whale at the time, if that is true, or swimming in the sea off Labrador, cannot deprive him of his rights at law. Indeed there is something to be said for Sir Roger Wheedle's contention that for a journalist comfortably placed in London to vilify the character of a public man who is in the belly of a whale off the coast of Labrador might well be a circumstance to be thrown into the scale in any assessment of damages.

Equally we must reject the somewhat unworthy suggestion of defendants' counsel that the entire affair was a 'publicity stunt' – or, alternatively, a plot to obtain damages from trusting newspapers. We cannot imagine a man so eager to secure mention, or money, from the newspapers that he will voluntarily step into sub-Arctic waters in foggy weather off the coast of Labrador. On the other hand, as we have indicated already, we cannot find it defamatory to say that a writer seeks publicity. The mere publication of a book is a request for public attention. Smith, therefore, and the General Press are dismissed from the action; though, since they have been rather a nuisance, they will pay the plaintiff's costs.

There remain the other defendants, and the other charges. These they have tediously attempted to justify by reference to the plaintiff's works, seeking to show that for this reason or that he is not worthy of regard as a composer of romantic fiction. Fortunately, I am relieved of any duty to go into all that by the defendants themselves, who have made so much of the story of the whale. After a strong attempt, and indeed inclination, to achieve credulity, I find myself unable to accept the story of the whale. But the manner in which the tale was told, and the doubts which I have felt concerning it, have persuaded me that the plaintiff is richly endowed with the qualities necessary for the writing of fiction, romantic or other

– with imagination, with the capacity to assemble corroborative details, and that indefinable power called plausibility. In short, it is clear to me that all the remaining defendants have libelled the plaintiff in his professional capacity, and they must pay damages, between them, of *about* £10,000 – or more, if the plaintiff wishes. What is the next case, please?

19 March 1947

Why is the House of Lords?

BOARD OF INLAND REVENUE v. HADDOCK

WE are able today to give some account of a startling judgment in the Court of Appeal delivered a few days before the end of term and, for reasons unknown but suspected, not hitherto reported in the Press.

The Master of the Rolls, having expressed a desire to hear no more argument from the learned counsel for the Crown, said:

This is an appeal from a judgment of a Divisional Court reversing an order by Quarter Sessions, allowing an appeal on a case stated from a decision of the magistrates granting an order to eject against an official of the Board of Inland Revenue upon a summons to show cause why the respondent should not have vacant possession of his own premises under an instruction of the Commissioners for Income Tax, afterwards reversed by the Board.

The point at issue is whether the appellants are entitled under the Land Tax Clauses of the Finance Act, 1931, to enter upon the window-box of the respondent, Mr Albert Haddock, and there remain for the purposes of measurement and assessment on the neglect or default of the respondent to supply particulars of his window-box upon the Land (Expropriation) Tax Form Q1/73198.

The point appears to be short and simple, but this Court does not intend to consider it. It will be observed from the history of the case as already recounted that a number of intelligent dispensers of justice have already addressed their minds to it with varying results. We are asked to say that the learned High Court judges who last considered the case were in error, and that the lay magistrates whose order they reversed were right. Whatever our decision, it is certain that an indignant appeal against it will be directed to the supreme tribunal, the House of Lords, since the resources of the Crown are as inexhaustible as its impudence, and the blood of Mr Haddock is evidently up.

In these circumstances, at the end of a long and fatiguing term of appeals, we do not feel called upon to consider this particular appeal with our customary care. But a few general observations upon our appellate system may not be out of place, and will at least satisfy the public that they are receiving full value from this distinguished Court.

The human mind is admittedly fallible, and in most professions the possibility of occasional error is admitted and even guarded against. But the legal profession is the only one in which the chances of error are admitted to be so high that an elaborate machinery has been provided for the correction of error – and not a single error, but a succession of errors. In other trades to be wrong is regarded as a matter for regret; in the law alone is it regarded as a matter of course. The House of Lords, as an appellate tribunal, is composed of eminent and experienced lawyers; but, if I may say so with respect, they are only by a small margin more eminent and experienced than the lawyers who compose this Court; indeed, it is frequently a matter of accident whether a judge selected for promotion is sent to this Court or reinforces the House of Lords. The difference in capacity is one of degree; indeed, the only real difference is that the House of Lords has the last word. But the difference in estimation is substantial, and in practice great issues and the destination of enormous sums of money are allowed to be determined by it.

Now, this is strange. The institution of one Court of Appeal may be considered a reasonable precaution; but two suggest panic. To take a fair parallel, our great doctors, I think, would not claim to be more respected or more advanced in their own science than our greatest jurists. But our surprise would be great if, after the removal of our appendix by a distinguished surgeon, we were taken before three other distinguished surgeons, who ordered our appendix to be replaced; and our surprise would give place to stupefaction if we were then referred to a tribunal of seven distinguished surgeons, who directed that our appendix should be extracted again. Yet such operations, or successions of operations, are an everyday experience in the practice of the law.

The moral, I think, is clear. A doctor may be wrong and he will admit it; but he does not assume that he will be wrong. In difficult or doubtful cases he will accept, and may even seek, the opinion of a colleague more experienced or expensive; but if he had to pronounce every opinion with the knowledge that in all probability it would be appealed against and publicly condemned as erroneous, there would be little confidence in the consulting-room on one side or the other, and few medical men would consent to continue in practice. Indeed, it says much for the patience and public spirit of our inferior judges that they devote such thought and labour to their work in these discouraging conditions, and show no resentment towards junior counsel who, at the close of a ten days' inquiry and a protracted judgment, inform the learned judge responsible for both that they will appeal against his decision.

In short, the existence side by side of the Court of Appeal and the appellate House of Lords appears to me to be indefensible in logic and unnecessary and even vicious in practice. If it be assumed that the House of Lords is in fact possessed of exceptional acuteness and knowledge of the law, it may well be said that every case of exceptional difficulty should have the benefit of these exceptional powers. But it follows from this that every such case should be certified at an early stage as one that can be usefully considered only by the House of Lords, and to that House it should be at once referred; just as a general practitioner in medicine, confronted with an obscure disease or unusual conditions outside the range of his experience and knowledge, will at once refer the sufferer to a specialist. But the litigant whose case is exceptionally complex cannot now avail himself of the supreme wisdom of the House of Lords until he has trailed his coat through a number of inferior Courts, which are *ex hypothesi* incompetent to secure his rights or remove his doubts. Which is evidently a waste of time and money.

But it is perhaps a generous assumption that the litigant thinks of the House of Lords as the possessor of exceptional wisdom. The very similar composition and capacity of that House and this Court, to which a respectful allusion has already been made, are well known to him; and that similarity must suggest to him that when the House of Lords thinks differently from us it is not so much evidence of their superior wisdom as a matter of luck. At the end of certain hotly contested cases, decided only by a majority in both the Court of Appeal and the House of Lords, the weary and impoverished litigant, adding up the number of judges who have voted for and against him in the various Courts, has found that, *per capita*, His Majesty's judges were equally divided on the point in dispute. It is not surprising, then, if many appellants present themselves to that House in a reckless or at least a speculative mood, as a gambler who has backed a succession of losers still hopes to recover all by a wild wager on the final race. The Court of Appeal, to one in this mood, must represent a minor handicap taking place at 3.30. It is not desirable that our great tribunals be regarded in this light; but at present it is inevitable. The people may be taught to believe in one Court of Appeal; but where there are two they cannot be blamed if they believe in neither. When a man keeps two clocks which tell the time differently, his fellows will receive with suspicion his weightiest pronouncements upon the hour of the day, even if one of them happens to be right. Moreover, the expense of successive appeals must make the acquisition of justice difficult for the rich and impossible for the poor. The unsuccessful litigant who cannot afford to go beyond the Court of Appeal must always be haunted by the thought that in the House of Lords he might have won; while the Inland Revenue, relying on the public purse, can pursue their unjust claims to the end and, if they lose, can send the bill to the taxpayer.

For all these reasons we recommend that either this Court or the House of Lords (as a Court of Appeal) be abolished; or, in the alternative, that the House of Lords retain its appellate functions as a specialist body for the settlement of questions of exceptional difficulty, such cases to be referred to them upon the order of a High Court judge. As for the present case, we decline to discuss it. It will go to the House of Lords in any event, so let it go at once. The appeal is formally allowed, and good luck to Mr Haddock!

Lord Justice Ratchet and Apple, J. concurred.

9 August 1933

Notes: 1. See '*In re* Macdonald' (*Uncommon Law*, page 352), where certain oddities of House of Lords procedure are discussed. For an appeal to the Lords the case for each side, till 1959, had to be presented in printed form, with a printed report of the proceedings in the inferior Courts. This did not reduce the cost of an appeal.

2. In 1945 your editor prepared, but was not allowed to present in the House of Commons, a 'Bill to expedite and cheapen the process of legal appeals'. It had a charming preamble:

Whereas it is necessary that the law be known and clear, but because of the costs of appeals or for other reasons the parties to a suit are not always able or willing to carry their case to the ultimate Court of Appeal, the House of Lords, so that important questions of law are left in doubt, and inferior courts are bound by decisions which are not apt to the changed conditions of the time . . .

and it provided that in certain circumstances appeals should go from the High Court to the House of Lords.

In 1947 an imposing Committee on Supreme Court Practice and Procedure was appointed. It sat for six industrious years under a superb Chairman, Sir Raymond Evershed, Master of the Rolls, nobly supported by three other judges (doing endless overtime for nothing) and nineteen others (of whom the editor was a bewildered and ineffective one). Among many other things, they recommended, in 1953, at page 331:

(131) In certain circumstances (i.e. where the question at issue is an important point essential to the determination of the case and is either (i) a question of the construction of a statute or statutory instrument which has been fully agreed before the Judge, or (ii) covered by a previous decision of the Court of Appeal, the validity of which it is desired to test, a Judge of the High Court should have power on application to certify that in the event of an appeal from his judgment the case is fit to 'leap-frog' the Court of Appeal and go direct to the House of Lords . . .

This looked like another loud 'I told you so' from Haddock:

but, alas, nothing happened. The end (in the House of Lords) of
pertinacious litigation by the Inland Revenue was reported on
18 January 1966. The taxpayer lost, of course – but look at the
score-card:

	For the Taxpayer	*For the Inland Revenue*
Mr Justice Ungoed-Thomas		1
Court of Appeal	3 Lord Justices[1]	
House of Lords	2 Lords of Appeal	3 Lords of Appeal
	—	—
	5	4

1. One dissenting in part.

The Tax on Virtue

AT the Old Bailey today Mr Justice Plush declined to allow this case, a prosecution by the Crown, to go to the jury. He said:

In this unusual and painful case the defendants are charged with a conspiracy to cause a public mischief by diminishing the revenue. The female defendant, May Merry, is a distinguished actress earning a considerable income of her own. The male defendant, Mr Pratt, is, or rather was, her husband, and he is a professor of economics, equally distinguished but not so prosperous. The couple lived happily together for fourteen years, and there was issue of the marriage three children.

Among their friends and neighbours they were regarded as a model couple; and in the spring of last year much surprise and consternation were caused by the news that the wife was filing a petition for a dissolution of marriage. The news was true, as it sometimes is, and a dissolution was duly decreed, the custody of the children being granted to the wife. But two days after the decree absolute was pronounced the two defendants again took up residence together in their London house; and there they have cohabited ever since, with their family, happily, according to the evidence, but technically in sin.

The writer of an anonymous letter brought these facts to the notice of the King's Proctor, who was asked to make an inquiry upon the ground that the divorce must have been obtained collusively or in other ways have been an abuse of the processes of law. The King's Proctor held that he was *functus officio*, that is, he had no status or excuse for interference in a matter which had been finally determined by the Court. The papers in the case showed without question that the divorce had been duly obtained according to the forms and practices of that queer branch of the law; but, not being wholly satisfied by his inquiries, he referred the matter to the Public Prosecutor.

The defendants, when challenged, made no secret of their position. Mr Pratt had caused himself to be divorced strictly according to the forms of law, in order to free himself from the excessive burden of income tax and surtax imposed upon him by the married state. While the couple were married their incomes were added together and assessed for taxation purposes as one income, and the impecunious husband was responsible for the tax upon the whole, though he was quite unable at law to get at a penny of his wife's money if she should see fit to withhold it. Further, though his own income never came near to the exalted regions of surtax or supertax, he was compelled by the bulking of the two incomes to pay supertax upon most of his own modest earnings; and if at any time his wife had declined to pay he might have been sent to prison for refusing to pay surtax on an income which has never qualified for it.

Resenting this position and without consulting his wife, he provided her with evidence which would formally justify her in seeking a divorce; and formally she took advantage of it. There is no evidence of connivance or collusion; and if there had been anything of the sort we must assume that the learned President of the Divorce Court would have discovered it. The wife may have known what was in the husband's mind after he took the fatal step, but it is not suggested that she knew before. The necessary facts were proved, and the motive of the parties is not material so far as the law of divorce is concerned; nor is there any law against a divorced couple living happily ever after.

The Crown, then, was in the familiar position of one who wants to find fault but cannot say why, smelling an offence but unable to identify it; and the Crown now says that the facts disclose an unlawful conspiracy not to defraud but to diminish the revenue. There is no doubt that the revenue has been diminished. Now that the parties are single they are separately assessed; each of them enjoys a 'personal allowance' of £100 instead of an allowance of £150 between them; Mr Pratt pays only the ordinary income tax upon his slender income; he is not responsible for the taxes on his wife's; and the total contribution to the revenue of the two of them is substantially less.

It is, no doubt, an undesirable thing to act deliberately in such a way as to diminish the revenue; but it need not necessarily be unlawful. A successful surgeon, for example, who decides that he will retire at forty and live quietly in a tub will diminish the revenue by the amount of the tax upon his former earnings. If we all decided to sell all that we have and give it to the poor we should cause an alarming fall in the revenue and probably an economic crisis. A solemn thought. But we should not be liable to an indictment for conspiracy.

In other words, it is an offence to evade income tax but not to avoid it. If every loving couple in the land decided that they would refrain from marriage because of the extra taxation which it involves they could not be punished by any existing law. Yet it would be a great mischief. For it has always been regarded as the public policy of the land that those who love each other should marry and have children. Accordingly the law of the land makes it easy to enter the married state but extremely difficult to leave it; and the children of married persons have still certain advantages (though these are diminishing) over the children of those who are not. There are various provisions which reflect the same policy – a contract or legacy, for example, restraining a person from marriage is void.

One would expect to find, then, that the law of income tax, being the only law that in the modern State has any real importance, would be framed in conformity with the same venerable policy; that it would say to Mr and Mrs Pratt, 'Since you have taken upon yourselves the responsibility of matrimony, the upkeep of a house and the rearing of a family, which are institutions dear to the State, you shall pay less by way of taxation than you would have paid if you had remained two independent celibates or lived together without the lawful tie.'

What we do find is the exact opposite. The State said to Mr Pratt, 'You are married, therefore you shall pay more.' And Mr Pratt replied, 'Then I will not be married.' In other words, we have here a direct conflict between a modern Act of Parliament and the public policy of the land as expressed in other Acts of Parliament and the principles of the Common Law. This is no new or exceptional thing; for many Acts of Parliament in these days appear to have been made by men walking

in their sleep – by a Legislature whose right hand is not aware
what its left hand doeth. If we are asked to enforce such statutes
we have no alternative but to obey. But the present case is
different. We are asked to extend the vague and elastic law of
conspiracy to cover a set of facts not hitherto contemplated – to
create, in effect, a new offence. We are not ready to do so. We
cannot find that at law the defendants have done anything
wrong. It is as if the State had said, 'You have a motor-car.
We shall tax you for it,' and the Pratts had replied, 'Then we
will get rid of the motor-car.'

Counsel for the Crown seemed to suggest that the defendants
had no cause for complaint, because together they were well off
and could afford to pay the extra taxes. But the principle is
the same whether the married persons are rich or poor. It is in
effect a tax upon marriage and a tax upon virtue, and no man
can be punished for evading such a tax unless Parliament expressly says so. It may be that the policy of Parliament has
changed and that marriage is to be regarded in future as a
taxable luxury. Without doubt much revenue could be extracted
from such a popular commodity. Marriages, like intoxicating
liquors, might be graded according to their strength; and the
most passionate, happy, or fruitful couples could be made to
pay more than the lukewarm or miserable. There are possi-
bilities here. But until Parliament has declared its will we are
bound by the Common Law.

I find that there is here no evidence of a Common Law
conspiracy, and I shall direct the jury to acquit the defendants.
Further, I think that they have done good service in drawing
attention to a grave evil, and I recommend that £6,000 be paid
to them out of public funds.

1 November 1933

Note: In 1965 there was serious talk in Whitehall and Westminster of abolishing the joint assessment, not for the sound
reasons outlined by Mr Justice Plush, but in order to encourage
married women to go out to work.

Why is a Jury?

BRITISH PHOSPHATES AND BEEF-EXTRACT, LTD *v.*
THE UNITED ALKALI AND GUANO SIMPLEX
ASSOCIATION

(Before Mr Justice Mole)

THIS complicated action has now lasted thirteen days. Sir Ethelred Rutt, K.C., whose health has recently been causing general concern, made a startling attack upon the jury in his closing speech for the plaintiff today. He said:

May it please your lordship, members of the jury, me learned friend has just completed an eloquent speech which continued for two days, and was at least one day too long. I must confess it wearied me . . .

Sir Humphrey Codd, K.C. (jumping up) : Milord . . .

The Judge : Be seated, Sir Humphrey. Sir Ethelred no doubt refers to the theme and not to the manner of your remarks.

Sir Ethelred : No, milord, I referred to the whole thing. But the passages which pained me most, members of the jury, were the sickly compliments he paid to you. At fairly regular intervals in his dreary recitations from documents and Law Reports he would break off to tell you that you were intelligent men and women and therefore you would think this; that you were men of the world and so would have noticed that; that you were reasonable, attentive, honourable, and God knows what, and so would certainly conclude the other. Perhaps he thought the only way in which he could hope to keep you awake was to throw bouquets at your heads. *What* a pie-face!

Sir Humphrey : Really, milord, I do protest . . .

The Judge : Calm yourself, Sir Humphrey. Counsel's language is not perhaps 'Parliamentary', but it is not unusual in a court of law. I think that you yourself described his client as a blackmailer and forger.

Sir Humphrey Codd became seated, muttering.

Sir Ethelred (continuing) : Now, ladies and gentlemen, I do not propose to slobber insincerities at you, though I too in my time have had occasion to wheedle a jury and drag out the *Vox Humana* stop in a closing speech. Of all the overrated contraptions in the British Constitution I rank highest – I mean lowest – the jury system. It may have been useful in the old days – and may be useful again – to protect the subject against a tyrannical Executive; and anyone who apprehends that he may receive injustice from a judge of the High Court sitting alone – a fantastic conception, milord – should be able to call for a jury to hear his cause. On some broad simple issues too – in libel actions, for example – a jury may help to keep the Courts in touch with modern opinion, though even there, as often as not, the verdict of twelve good men and true is false and wicked, staggering and crazy. But in a case . . .

The Judge : Sir Ethelred, will there be any charge for your lecture on the jury system?

Sir Ethelred : No, milord. Milord, I was just coming to the present case. Look at it! It's lasted a fortnight. The most complicated dispute in my experience. The documents were a mile high when we began; and they now measure three, for the reports of the proceedings in this Court amount to two (to which the speeches of me learned friend, milord, have contributed about half a mile) . . .

Sir Humphrey : Milord . . .

Sir Ethelred : All about debentures and mergers and mortgages and subsidiary companies – twenty-five subsidiary companies on one side alone! Not to mention the expert evidence about the scientific stuff – all that *fandango* about the magnesium alkaloid and the patent vapour-feed. The chemists on the two sides flatly contradicted each other, and so did the accountants. I don't believe there's an accountant on either side who really knows what some of the figures mean; I don't believe there's a single person in this Court . . .

The Judge : There is one person in this Court, Sir Ethelred, who has a firm grasp of the whole case.

Sir Ethelred : I beg your lordship's pardon. Certainly, milord. But, milord, with great respect, that rather bears out –

ah – what I was saying – ah – for that one person, milord, as this is a jury case, will not have to answer the important questions in the case. You, milord, have had the advantage at every stage of this protracted bicker of seeing the shorthand reports of the previous day's proceedings, with copies of the material documents, diagrams, maps, schedules, balance-sheets, accounts, and so forth. So, milord, have me learned friend and myself, each of whom is attended by a small cloud of solicitors and junior counsel. We are all three possessed of exceptional intelligence and are equipped by long training and practice for the rapid understanding of complex figures and affairs; and if at any moment we are in doubt we can request each other or our advisers for information and assistance. Yet you will recall, milord, how often we have found ourselves – sometimes all three of us – in an incontestable fog about some vital point, exactly what a witness said or a correspondent wrote, the date of an interview, the amount of a cheque or bribe, the wording of a formula, the position of a building; and how many minutes we have spent each day upon excavating the forgotten facts from the desert of documents with which we are surrounded. And how, milord, can we expect these twelve poor mutts on the jury . . .

The Judge : What is a mutt?

Sir Ethelred : Milord, a mutt . . .

The Judge : Sir Ethelred, no doubt you know best the lines of advocacy most likely to advance the interests of your clients; but is it quite wise to describe the jury as 'mutts', which, though I am not familiar with it, I judge instinctively to be a term of depreciation?

Sir Ethelred : Milord, 'mutt' is a relative term. The Prime Minister, if he were requested to transpose a musical composition in A flat major into the key of E minor would readily confess himself a mutt in relation to that particular task.

The Judge : Very well, Sir Ethelred. Proceed.

Sir Ethelred (turning to the jury) : How, I say, can you poor mutts be expected to get a grip of this colossal conundrum *without the assistance of any documents at all*? No shorthand notes, no maps, no accounts, except now and then when his lordship decides it is time you were given a bone to play with, and we let you have a hasty glance at a diagram that doesn't matter. The whole thing's fantastic! There you sit on your hard seats, with scarcely room to wriggle, wondering what it is all about. Decent fellows, I dare say, some of you, but with no particular intelligence or financial training, and wildly divergent in character and opinion. And presently his lordship will ask you to answer – and answer *unanimously* – about seventeen extremely unanswerable questions: 'Did the defendant knowingly make a false assertion?' and so forth. How the deuce do you know? You don't even know when you've made a false assertion yourselves. And *unanimous*! I look at you, twelve good men and true – or rather, ten good men and true and two women[1] – and I try to think of any simple subject about which the twelve of you would be likely to agree unanimously if you were assembled together by chance in any place outside this Court; at a dinner-party, on a committee. The simplest questions of fact, morals, ethics, history, arithmetic – and you'd be all over the shop.[2] And yet when we shut you up in a cold room with nothing to eat you can arrive at unanimous decisions about questions that baffle the wisest brains of the Bench and Bar. I find that highly suspicious. I don't believe . . .

The Judge : Do the jury wish Sir Ethelred to continue?

The Foreman of the Jury : Yes, milord; we find the gentleman refreshing.

The Judge : Then perhaps Sir Ethelred will make a gradual approach towards the case which is before us?

Sir Ethelred : No, milord, that is just the point. Members of the jury, for the reasons adumbrated I consider it quite idle to discuss this difficult case with you at all. Though I spoke with the tongues of men and of angels and for as long as me learned friend, it would still be a complete gamble which side you came

1. Not, perhaps, a necessary or chivalrous distinction.
2. See *Haddock* v. *Mansfield*, where a jury found that it was not defamatory to say that a modern novel was 'objectionable, filthy, and immoral', though they did not think that this was a reasonable description of the book in question. And see Wedderburn on *Women Jurors*.

down on. For all I know, the gentleman with the strongest personality in that box may particularly dislike me or have a warm admiration for Sir Humphrey Codd. One of us two is right in this case and represents truth and honesty; the other does not: and all I propose to tell you is that I am the one who is right. But I will fortify that bald assertion with the reminder that I have at least, to your knowledge, told the truth about me learned friend, about the jury system, and about yourselves. Which is more than Sir Humphrey can say. And I ask you to argue that if I am demonstrably truthful and right about so much I am probably truthful and right about the rest. Good afternoon.

The Foreman: We find for the plaintiff.

The Judge: But I haven't summed up! This will take three days.

The Foreman: Milord, it is not necessary. We are all sure Sir Ethelred is right. Milord, it is the wish of the jury to give three hearty cheers for Sir Ethelred Rutt!

The Judge: Oh, very well. Judgment for the plaintiff. This jury must not serve again.

5 April 1933

Note: The learned counsel seems to have left out of account the point of view of the jurors. In a recent case (*Cole* v. *The Chiswick Sewage Farm*) it was found on the third day of the hearing that one of the jury was stone-deaf and had not understood a word of the proceedings. When asked why he had not revealed the fact before, he said that he had enjoyed watching the lawyers and thought he was doing no harm. 'I am sorry to go, because I liked the job,' remarked the juryman as he left the box. 'I have not heard a word, but I liked being here. I am sorry I forgot to say I was deaf.' To serve on a jury is to be free from the telephone, the tax-collector, from noise and other troubles for a much longer period than most citizens ever enjoy in ordinary life. See the *Memoirs of a Dramatist* (Ballock & Co.), where Mr Athol Fitch records that he wrote two plays during the judge's summing-up in *British Fuel Oil, Ltd.* v. *The University of London* (1926).

How Free is a Freeman?

THE CORPORATION OF BURBLETON *v*. STANISLAVSKI

MR JUSTICE PLUSH today gave judgment in this unusual action which raises a question of interest to many townships at the present time. His Lordship said:

In this action the Corporation of Burbleton City are proceeding – reluctantly, as they have assured us, and we can well believe – against Marshal Stanislavski, the distinguished commander who has done so much for the cause of the Allied Nations in Eastern Europe. So sensible of his deeds and services were the people of Burbleton that they decided to confer upon him the Freedom of Burbleton. Accordingly, in a moving ceremony this year, the young Marshal was made an honorary Freeman of the Borough. There was a banquet; there were noble speeches; there was a procession, during which the excited citizens swarmed affectionately about the Marshal's car.

These emotions had scarcely subsided when, to the surprise and delight of the citizens, it was announced that the Marshal proposed to take up his residence in the first city to make him a freeman. Burbleton is by the sea, the Marshal is fond of swimming and boating; and in his own country, it appears, even a Marshal is subject to so many restraints and restrictions that the status of freeman (unknown in his own land) made a very practical appeal to him. The grateful citizens purchased and presented to the Marshal a fine freehold mansion beside the sea; and there he resides.

Unfortunately, at no stage was it made clear to anyone or by anyone exactly what the privileges of a freeman are, which is indeed the question the Court has now to answer. Some light, but not much, emerges from a study of the Honorary Freedom of Boroughs Act, 1885. It is there laid down that persons of eminence may be made Honorary Freemen of a Borough, with a proviso that the persons so distinguished shall not be entitled to share in the produce or the proceeds of a sale of any property or stocks belonging to the Corporation.

This purely negative information does not lead us very far. Counsel for the plaintiffs has urged persuasively that the word 'honorary' is equivalent to 'formal', that the whole affair is no more than a symbolic courtesy and that no substantial privileges are in fact or law conferred by it. The Court rejects this view. We are satisfied that the word 'honorary' is used in distinction from the old, and now forbidden, practice by which it was possible to purchase the status of freeman. Further, putting the best construction, as we feel bound to do, on the acts of a municipal corporation, we decline to assume that this and other bodies can have performed with so much pomp and circumstance an act that was practically meaningless.

Sir Roger Wheedle, K.C. (for the Corporation): Milord, if I may – with great respect – I think my clients might reasonably take exception to the expression 'meaningless'. The public display of goodwill, the generous refreshments, the illuminated address, the casket . . .

The Judge: Yes, yes, Sir Roger. But what I said was 'practically' meaningless. That, at all events, was the view taken by the Marshal, who argued simply that a freeman must be more free than one who was not a freeman, especially if he was made free with so much ceremony and emotion.

On the first Wednesday after his arrival he drove out in his car to shop in the narrow High Street of the city. On that day, by the by-laws, it was the turn for motor-cars to park on the west side of the street. The Marshal, however, left his car, unattended, on the east side, while he conducted with considerable gaiety, and even familiarity, a long conversation with a comely shop-assistant. A big and intractable traffic-jam resulted. The Marshal emerged at last to find a curious crowd, two stern policemen, and a long line of vehicles, all hooting indignantly. When the identity of the delinquent was recognized, however, the scowls of the citizens gave way to smiles. The policeman, in simple terms, explained the bye-law; the Marshal said charmingly, 'I have understood – but I am

Freeman – is it not?' and the incident passed off with good humour.

The next day the Marshal was seen driving very fast along the sea-front, on the wrong side of the road, ignoring the lights, singing a wild old cavalry song, and with a young lady on his knee. When stopped at last and chided by a constable, he said again, with his delightful smile: 'But I am Freeman of Borough – yes?' The officer, with singular tact and intelligence, remarked that the Marshal was a Freeman of Burbleton, but not of Great Britain, and that neither the Corporation nor anyone else could give him licence to violate the general traffic-laws of the kingdom. The Marshal, according to the evidence, took the point at once; and has not since offended in this manner.

The distinction made by the constable, however, may well have fortified the Marshal's evident belief that within the bounds of the Borough he was entitled to ignore the obligations of a citizen of the Borough. There followed, at brief intervals, a series of incidents which have caused disquiet. The first was the great soldier's resolute refusal to pay any rates. A Freeman, he said, must surely enjoy the public services of the Borough – the police, the gas, the water, and so on, free of charge. There seems to be some reason in this contention, and the Corporation at length assented.[1] Similarly, with success, the Marshal declined to make any payment for entry onto the Victory Pier, or for the use of a deck-chair on the Esplanade.

Next came the Rocket Episode. On the fifteenth anniversary of the foundation of the Revolutionary State in his own land the Marshal gathered a number of his compatriots in the evening on the Esplanade. A great many toasts were drunk; a small but active balalaika band played stirring folk-songs, in which the chorus joined, interfering no little with the efforts of the municipal band to please the citizens not far away; and there was a fine display of that acrobatic form of dancing described by one witness as 'dancing sitting down'.

Rockets and other fireworks were then produced and dis-

    1. Before the Municipal Corporations Act, 1935, which respected existing usages, a Freeman was exempt from all 'tolls and dues'.

charged: and finally the Marshal fired one hundred and one live rounds into the air from his revolver in honour of the Revolution. There is, it appears, a very strict by-law against the use of fireworks on the Esplanade; and one of the rockets discharged at a low angle set fire to the head of the Pier. The fire was quickly extinguished, and for this part of the evening's work the Marshal charmingly expressed regret; but, as to the rest, he again genially reminded the authorities that he was a Freeman.

The Marshal has a large steam yacht which he has berthed in the Harbour, refusing to shift his berth when desired, or to pay any harbour-dues. The Corporation is rightly proud of the various by-laws and regulations which it has established to keep the practice of sea-bathing within decent and orderly limits. No undressing on the beach, not even 'macintosh-bathing', is permitted: and all must enter the sea from Corporation huts, within well-defined limits and in standard costumes. The Marshal and his friends have consistently ignored these arrangements. Hilarious parties of young men and women have emerged from his house and noisily entered the sea at all hours of the day and night, in costumes variously described as bizarre, scanty, and Continental, and, on at least one occasion, it is rumoured, in no costumes at all. And the mischief is, say the Corporation, that some of their own citizens are inclining towards indiscipline too.

These assaults upon public order and the decent name of Burbleton at last provoked the Council to firmer action than they had cared to contemplate before. With admirable tact they caused to be conveyed to the Marshal a private intimation that unless he could find it convenient to comply with the local by-laws, customs and charges his presence in the Borough would be no longer welcome. The Marshal replied laughingly, 'But I am Freeman. The people love me.' Which appears to be true.

What are the Corporation to do? They cannot eject him, for he is a freeholder. It would be odious to prosecute the great man whom they have delighted to honour, for what many would think to be small offences. Moreover, they are not sure of their position at law: and they have come to this Court for a declaration.

The Court holds, with some reluctance, that they have brought this trouble on themselves. By the way, does the Marshal get a vote?

Mr Mould (for the Marshal) : The rights and privileges of a Freeman, milord, in the old days, generally included the right to vote at a Parliamentary election of the borough. Whether a Freeman of foreign birth . . .

The Judge: Well, there you are. There must be some substantial significance in the appellation 'Freeman', or it would not have been made the subject of an Act of Parliament. That significance can only be a degree of freedom within the Borough not enjoyed by the citizen who is not a freeman. Discretion and taste will, no doubt, in most cases suggest the limits within which such a privilege shall be enforced; but, so long as he does not infringe the law of the land, we hold that in Burbleton the Marshal can do what he likes.

4 July 1945

End of a Nonsense

I

THE House of Lords today discussed a conundrum on the
law of defamation which has long provoked and puzzled our
leading jurists. The Lord Chancellor said:

This is an appeal by Sir Wesley Trout, M.P., from a decision
by the Court of Appeal (Lord Justice Rutt dissenting) reversing
a decision of Mr Justice Plush in the Queen's Bench Division.
The facts are simple. The appellant, a retired man of business,
stood for Parliament at the recent by-election for Hammerton
(West). He was 'adopted' not long before the election, was
new to the neighbourhood, as well as to political life, and had
little time to captivate the fifty thousand electors. The respondent company offered their aid. The ordinary methods, they
said, of poster, canvassing, and public meeting, always expensive and exhausting, would in his case be quite ineffective
as well: for if he travelled and talked all day and all night he
would still be unable to make his presence, his personality, and
opinions, sufficiently felt. They suggested, therefore, the use of
the air. One plan was to fly a helicopter slowly over Hammerton, at the lawful height, and to lower the candidate, by a long
rope to roof-level, or near it, in a comfortable chair, from which
he could address the unfortunate citizens without fear of
interruption or correction, through the barbarous instrument
known as a 'loud-hailer'. This, as your Lordships heard with
horror, was successfully done more than once. Another plan,
which is the cause of this litigation, was to advertise the
candidate's name and nobility over the borough by a procedure known as 'sky-writing'. Here, it appears, an aircraft picks
out some simple message in huge letters formed of smoke or
vapour, high in the sky. Whatever the message, the spectacle

of the soaring machine is sure to capture the attention of every street for many miles. The respondents first sent up a pilot, Mr Broot, to 'write' upon the pale-blue dome of heaven the words ALL OUT FOR TROUT; and this was a big success, doing more to get the candidate's name into the people's heads than numerous posters and meetings. The next was TROUT IS ALWAYS RIGHT. Unhappily there was a calligraphic error, and the last word began with a T, making it TIGHT. It was a fine still day, the message hung in the sky for half an hour, and was read by vast hilarious crowds. The pilot apologized, no malice was suspected – after all, a man flying at a great height, vertically or upside-down, may easily make literal mistakes – and the next day Mr Broot was ordered aloft again. This time the message was SEND TROUT IN: but the appellant was horrified, and the crowds were delighted, when the last word was done, to read SEND TROUT GIN. 'What a bungler!' thought the innocent appellant: and that was all he thought. The machine passed onto another part of the sky where it was to write a second battle cry: VOTE FOR TROUT THE PUBLIC FRIEND. This, according to the respondent company, was designed as a pleasant parallel to 'the Public Trustee' and a sly reply to the tall talk of Sir Wesley's rival about the benefits of Public Ownership. But the respondent Broot wrote clearly on the sky VOTE FOR TROUT THE PUBLICANS FRIEND. (He even tried, according to the evidence, to depict an apostrophe after the 's' in PUBLICANS.) He then flew off to a distant airfield, landed, and left the country at once.

Later, it emerged that Broot was a supporter of a small but subversive political party, and had a personal spite against Sir Wesley, from one of whose factories he had been dismissed some years earlier. 'Celestial Publicity Limited' were innocent, in fact, but were technically responsible for Mr Broot's behaviour: and Sir Wesley sued both for defamation. Sir Wesley is not, in fact, a teetotaller, and indeed is reasonably tolerant of the use of alcohol (as wine is now described), but no more. The seat is a 'safe' one, and the accusations in the sky were not enough to lose it: but he complains they have stuck. Small boys cry after him, 'Boozer!' or 'Trout, the human fish!' On the other hand many electors, it seems, thought the better of him: and many who did not, thought that he had been hardly used and voted accordingly.

The trouble is – not for his country, we may be sure, but for himself – that he was successful in the election. Nor, having 'retired', can he claim that he has been injured in any professional capacity. In other words, he could offer no evidence that he has suffered any actual damage from the celestial insults of which he complains. That would not matter if they were indubitably in the nature of libel, if Mr Broot had written his foul words on a postcard or published them in a newspaper. For then, damage or no, he, and his employers, without any doubt, would be liable: and such was the finding of Mr Justice Plush. But the respondents claim that the defamation, if any, was no more than a slander, so that some damage must be shown: and such was the finding of the majority of the Court of Appeal (Lord Justice Rutt dissenting).

Your Lordships, then, must wearily consider once more the question to which, for so many decades, so many judges, juries, and jurists have given so much time, thought and toil: have we here a libel or a slander? We shall, I fear, be discussing it for many decades more: for a Defamation Bill, now well on its way to the Statute Book, does little to modify, and nothing to remove, an old but accidental distinction which many good minds regard as vicious and valueless, which does not exist in Scotland, but is preserved like a sacred relic in this part of our island.

My Lords, I need not tell you, but I must – for the instruction of less learned men and the full employment of typists and printers – what that distinction is. Upon the best authority, a text-book, in libel the defamatory statement is made in some permanent and visible form, such as writing, printing, or effigies: in slander it is made in spoken words or in some other transitory form, whether visible or audible, such as gestures, hissing, or other inarticulate but significant sounds.

In which category are we to place insults which are conveyed by smoke or vapour high above the earth's surface? They are

visible: they are in the form of legible letters: they are described by the respondents themselves as 'writing' of a sort.
But they are certainly not 'permanent'; they begin to dwindle
as soon as they are made, and in ordinary conditions of wind
and weather are not decipherable, perhaps, for more than
ten minutes. After that they are a memory, no more. No man
can say to his wife or child 'Come out and see what they have
written about Trout'; for there is nothing to see. Vapour is
not like a postcard, a paper, a caricature, which can be passed
from hand to hand. It is much more like a rude word, or
derogatory speech, 'gone with the wind', or, in the words of the
authorities, 'transitory in form'. On the other hand, these
particular insults were conveyed to the minds of millions and
will remain there longer, it may be, than anything that they
read on a postcard or even in a newspaper. My Lords, I think
it will be convenient if we now have lunch and continue our
discussion on another day.

The House adjourned.

2

The House of Lords considered again the appeal of Sir
Wesley Trout, M.P., in the Sky-writing Case. Sir Wesley
complained of defamatory messages 'written' in the sky, in
vapour, during a by-election. The Lord Chancellor, continuing, said:

It is not disputed that the smoke-signals or characters were
defamatory. The only question is, are they libel, as was held
by Mr Justice Plush, or slander, as the Court of Appeal (Lord
Justice Rutt dissenting) decided? Should they be treated as
'permanent', like a letter or postcard, or 'transitory', like a
hiss, hoot, or derogatory speech? In the first case the appellant
will receive the damages awarded by the Court of first instance:
in the second his suit will be at last dismissed.

Learned counsel have referred us to some cases of which all
that can be said is that they belong to the same department of

doubt. There was the famous case of *Chicken* v. *Ham*,[1] where a man deliberately caused opprobrious words to be recorded and published by means of a gramophone. There were two trials of the action and two appeals to the Court of Appeal, which held on the first occasion that the wrong was slander and on the second that it was libel. In your Lordships' House my illustrious predecessor and Lord Arrowroot were for slander, and the late Lords Lick and Sheep for libel: the late Lord Goat was about to give his opinion, which would, presumably, have been decisive, when, unhappily, he perished of heart failure. The second of two contradictory decisions of the Court of Appeal, therefore, was allowed to stand, precariously – a not entirely satisfactory climax to an enjoyable year or two of litigation.

Lord Lick in that appeal referred to the case of *Silvertop* v. *Stepney Guardians*, 'where a man trained a parrot to say three times after meals "Councillor Wart has not washed today." It was held that this was a libel.' A minor jurist has unworthily complained that no record is to be found of *Silvertop* v. *Stepney Guardians*. But the learning and character of the late Lord Lick are too well respected . . .

Lord Wool: It was one of Lick's own cases. I know what happened. There was a fire that night at the reporter's house. Old Lick could hardly remember his name: but he never forgot his own judgments. The parrot's all right.

The Lord Chancellor: Just so. The House is obliged to Lord Wool. But the repetitive parrot – like the repetitive gramophone – has an element of continuity which cannot be found in brief and fugitive vapour-writing. Then there was the more recent case of *Temper* v. *Hume and Haddock*.[2] There the insults were conveyed by flag-signals in the International Code, the flags being displayed sometimes for a few minutes only, sometimes for a few hours at most. Here, you may think, we are nearer to temporary defamation by vapour. Unhappily, the jury disagreed about the facts, and Mr Justice Codd (now defunct) was unable, or perhaps unwilling, to pronounce an opinion on the

1. *Uncommon Law*, page 71.
2. Page 23, and 'Codd's Last Case', page 125.

question of law. Your Lordships have never had a similar case before you, and so have no decision of your own to guide you. Parliament has declined to abolish the distinction between libel and slander: and your Lordships, I conceive, are bound to abide by it. I think that this was a slander, and the appeal should be dismissed.

Lord Wool: Stuff and nonsense! With great respect to my noble friend the Lord Chancellor, I disagree. Not only with what he said but the way he said it. Evidently he doesn't like the Common Law: but he's afraid to say so. I'm not. God bless me! Who made the Common Law? The judges. Who are we? The top judges. And who's put the Common Law right when it's old and silly? Why, we of course. I thought it pitiful to see our good Lord Chancellor prowling about, like a dog at the dustbins, in the Courts below, trying to find some mouldy old decision to comfort him. Then he bleated that Parliament had not abolished the crazy quibbles about libel and slander. Well, it has done a bit, just a nibble or two. But we invented them, and we should put an end to them. You're all afraid. I'm not. I'm 73. But I'll race any of you across Westminster Bridge. Where was I? Oh yes. You say, in this case, there was 'no actual damage'. Therefore the poor chap can't recover. God bless me, isn't it enough to have small boys calling 'Boozer!' after you? How would any of your Lordships like it? I don't care whether you call this libel or slander – it was defamation, the man has suffered, and the appeal should be allowed.[1]

Lord Middle: I do not agree. It will be a sad day for British justice if ever we interrupt the orderly march of precedent and case-law. Nor can I dismiss so lightly as Lord Wool the ancient distinction between written and spoken abuse or vilification. It does not, I know, exist in Scottish law: but then, I understand, most of the Scots are more or less speechless. In England, everywhere, it would be disastrous if a writ could issue for

---

1. 'One thing the Lord Chancellor's less patient critics want him to do without delay is to abolish the whole "doctrine of precedents" . . . Justinian wiped it out altogether. We ought to do the same.' C. H. Rolph, *New Statesman*, 28 January 1965.

every foolish or unfriendly word. Turning to the present appeal, I find, like the Lord Chancellor, that insults in smoke or vapour have not the solid and enduring character which is required in a case of libel. They are more like the signal-flags, and less like the trained parrot or the gramophone, both of which, I should say, were libellous. This was a slander and the appeal should be dismissed.

The House adjourned. The score is now 2–1. Lords Off and Laburnum have still to give their opinions. In legal circles the betting is heavy, and most of the money is on slander.

3

The House of Lords considered for the third day the Sky-writing Case, in which Sir Wesley Trout, M.P., claims damages for defamatory messages expressed in smoke. Lord Wool, at the last hearing, vigorously declared himself in Sir Wesley's favour: but the Lord Chancellor and Lord Middle came down on the side of slander – and the respondents. Score 2–1. Betting 6–4 on slander.

Lord Off : I do not agree. I have reached the same conclusion as Lord Wool, but by a different route. He is not, I think, quite just to the judges of the past. The distinction of which he complains is due to an historical accident. Slander, in ancient days, was dealt with by the feudal, and later by the ecclesiastical courts. Then printing came in, and the apprehensive Star Chamber made the new invention its particular care, so that an action for libel has retained some of the criminal character of that Court's proceedings, and no proof of damage is required. We should still, I think, make some distinction between garden-wall gossip and widespread defamation. The trouble is that our distinctions are now out of date. Other mechanical inventions have followed printing, and there may be more to come: but the Courts, having no guidance from your Lordships' House, are still applying the ancient rules of the Common Law which are evidently inappropriate to the age of the gramophone, the film, the talking-film, the radio, the loud-hailer, and now the sky-scribbler. The test should be not the method, or even the duration, but the area and the occasion of the defamatory act. The Bill now before Parliament goes a little way in this direction. 'The broadcasting of words by means of wireless telegraphy' is to be treated as 'publication in permanent form'.[1] But this will not assist the man who is vilified by loud-hailer, gramophone or sky-writer. In my judgment, wherever a mechanical instrument is employed, the area and the importance of the defamatory act is likely to be greater (about the trained parrot I express no opinion), and the wrong should therefore be considered more offensive in degree, and, for convenience, *prima facie*, be classed as libel. I find that there was here a libel, and the appeal should be allowed.

The score was now two Law Lords all, with one to go. Excitement was intense as the aged Lord Laburnum began to speak. He said:

My Lords, I am only 87: but I am not going to race my brother Wool across Westminster Bridge. Still, my memory's pretty good. My mind goes back more than twenty years – I think it was 1928 or '9 – to the case of *Sparrow* v. *Pipp*,[2] where your Lordships' House (including myself) stood by a young puppy of a puisne judge who had cocked a snook at the Common Law of defamation. His name was Wool. The Lord Chancellor of those days – I forget his name – used language very different from that which has fallen from the noble occupant of the Woolsack today. He said: 'Your Lordships have the power to amend the Common Law provided that you are willing to abandon in some degree the mechanical adhesion to precedent which has been for centuries the foundation of our judicial practice. We may as well begin with the law of libel.' Very good. But here we are, twenty-four years later, still splitting the same old hairs. Of course – and here I agree with Wool – the simplest thing is to stop all this talk about 'special

1. Sections 1, 2, 3, of Defamation Act 1952.
2. *Uncommon Law*, p. 153.

damage'; then we could stop distinguishing between libel and slander. Why should a man have to prove that he has lost a job or been turned out of a club? Damage to reputation, to character, to pride, is not a material thing to be measured and calculated like damage to a motor-car, or the supply of gas to a house. If many people have been led to believe bad things about you which are not true that should be enough. My Lords, you are all afraid of letting loose a lot of flimsy and frivolous actions, I know: but judges and juries can be trusted to discourage those. Let's do a little deeming. My Lords, I declare the law to be as follows: In these times there is no libel, there is no slander; there is only defamation. In any clear case of defamation it shall be deemed that there is damage, whether spiritual or material, 'actual' or 'special', until the contrary is shown. After all, if a man hits you in the face you do not have to prove that you are dead or disabled. It is sufficient that there has been an unjust and unprovoked assault. Of course, if the defamatory defendant can show that the plaintiff has suffered little or nothing the plaintiff may be discouraged with costs: but the scurrilous defendant will be discouraged too. People will be more careful what they say, and litigation, in my opinion, will be less, not more. In this case I deem accordingly. The appeal should be allowed and Sir Wesley Trout should have his damages.

It was. He did.

29 October 1952

Note: Here is an instructive picture of the stately progress of law reform in our land. In 1935, in his first Election Address, your editor wrote: 'The *law of libel* is full of uncertainty and illogicality and should be drastically reformed . . . in the Age of Radio the distinction between libel and slander is manifestly indefensible.' In 1938 (and 1939) he presented a Bill, which, among other things, proposed to assimilate the two. The Government referred it to the distinguished Porter Committee, who, by a majority, said No. Two dissentients, though, Mr Richard O'Sullivan, K.C., and Professor E. C. S. Wade (bless them!) were on my side:

They consider that no adequate reason now exists for perpetuating a distinction which originated by an accident of legal history, finds no place in Scots law, and has led to a confusing volume of case-law.

The Porter Committee reported in 1948. Then everyone went to sleep again. The Government did nothing at all. But in 1951, on his own initiative, a private Member, Mr N. H. Lever, Labour, presented a Bill founded on the Porter Report, and your editor applauded his labours with a grandfather's interest and pride. His Defamation Act received the Royal Assent on 30 October 1952, a day after the decision in Trout's case.

Section 2 materially modified the distinction between libel and slander but not to the extent demanded by Lord Laburnum. The Section reads:

In an action for slander in respect of words calculated to disparage the plaintiff in any office, profession, calling, trade or business held or carried on by him at the time of the publication it shall not be necessary to allege or prove special damage, whether or not the words are spoken of the plaintiff in his office, profession, calling, trade or business.

This is a great improvement of the law, and shows that Parliament had taken note of the long series of cases mentioned by the Lord Chancellor in Trout's case. Whether the new Section would have saved the plaintiff Trout his protracted and expensive litigation, is not absolutely certain. He was not 'at the time of the publication' holding any 'office' for he had not yet been elected. Nor, having retired, had he any 'trade or business'. But is a politician, seeking election to Parliament, 'carrying on . . . a profession or calling'? Presumably yes. But an unscrupulous defendant might well have argued that Trout, who had never sought election before, was not entitled to the benefit of the Section. More interesting litigation may be expected, and it would have been better, many feel, if Parliament had made a clean sweep of the distinction.

On 26 July 1966 the Lords announced that, while treating former decisions of the House as normally binding, they would depart from a previous decision when it appeared right to do so.

Bookmakers All

REX *v*. HADDOCK AND VINE

'ONE of the most shameless frauds on the Revenue ever conceived,' said the Attorney-General, Sir Anthony Slatt, in his final address to the jury at the Old Bailey today. 'You will know what to do,' he concluded grimly.

Mr Justice Codd, summing-up to the jury, said:

The learned Attorney-General has allowed himself to become more excited than is customary in counsel prosecuting for the Crown. That, in the circumstances of this case, is understandable: but you must not allow his emotion to affect you. Nor should you be swayed by the almost universal loathing for the prisoner Haddock. Address your minds to the facts, and to so much of the law as I am able to explain.

No excitement was caused, a year or two ago, when the ancient and respected firm of Lotwood put the words 'Bookmakers and' before the word 'Publishers' on their fine building and elegant notepaper. After all, it is part of their business, as the Memorandum of Association says, to 'prepare, devise, make and manufacture' books: and the addition was thought, by the few who noticed it, to be an unnecessary but pardonable essay in precision.

But one of Lotwoods' authors is the notorious Albert Haddock who stands before you in that dock today. This man is chiefly known for his unreasoning and unrelenting objection to the rates of income tax and the methods of the selfless officers whose duty it is to assess and collect it. But again, members of the jury, though, as good citizens yourselves, you may delight and glory in the income tax, I must adjure you to put aside such odious sentiments as may naturally arise in you towards weak, eccentric characters who do not think as you do.

In February this year the officers of the Inland Revenue Department were placidly planning, according to law, to take

away from Albert Haddock two-thirds or more of the money
he had earned by his brains and labour in the two preceding
years. During their kindly researches into his banking account
– which, to do the prisoner full justice, was offered for their
inspection – they came upon a 'credit' entry of £1,000, a
cheque signed for that amount by Mr Stanley Vine, the
general manager of Lotwoods. 'This,' they said, 'is, we pre-
sume, part of your professional earnings, an "advance on
royalties" for one of your books, perhaps?' 'No, no,' said the
prisoner; 'that was my winnings on a successful bet – and,
therefore, is not subject to income tax.' 'What was the bet?'
said the officer. 'That,' said the prisoner, 'has nothing to do
with you. I do a good deal of betting with Mr Vine,' he added,
and he indicated in the bank-book several small payments to
Mr Vine. These, he said, were for unsuccessful bets on horses
and dogs. You snorted at that, didn't you, Sir Anthony?

The Attorney-General: Milord?

The Judge: Never mind. The Inland Revenue then visited
the Lotwood office, where the prisoner Vine, it appears, was
as frank and open as he has been in the box. The Memorandum of Association says that the company may conduct
'any other business whatsoever which can be advantageously
carried on by the company'; and side by side with the ordinary
business of producing and marketing books in the literary
sense his firm are now conducting the business of a credit
'bookmaker', in the sporting sense. So far as the Court knows,
there is no objection to this in law. Many citizens, including
the prisoner Haddock, and at least two Royal Commissions,
have recommended that all 'bookmakers' should be registered
and licensed. But the Legislature has never thought fit to
provide for this. Indeed, in these days, it is about the only
thing that can be done without a licence. Anyone, therefore,
can set himself up as a bookmaker, if he so desire, and, provided he sticks to credit-betting, and does not allow persons
to resort to his office for the purpose of betting, nobody can
interfere with him. Of course, he will have to produce his accounts to the Inland Revenue and pay tax upon his profits,
if any.

Further, as counsel for the defence have suggested, you may think that there is a special affinity between these two types of business. As the prisoner Vine told the Court, 'Nothing could be more like a gamble than the production and sale of works of art.' Some of Vine's bets, it seems, have been directly connected with the other branch of the business. Authors, he told us, are sometimes idle, sometimes temperamental, always uncertain. He may sign with them a generous contract for the production of a novel in time for the spring season, with an advance on royalties to be paid on delivery of the manuscript. Paper is bought: the printers stand ready. Years pass; no novel appears: and there is nothing he can do about it. But such febrile characters, he says (and, after all, he should know the psychology of his business best), are often stimulated by the challenge of a bet. Accordingly, sometimes, he will bet Author A £500 that he will *not* deliver his new book by April 30. Author A, as a rule, he says, roars into action, toils day and night, produces the book on time, and wins the bet – to the advantage of all concerned.

The £1,000 payment to the prisoner Haddock, it was revealed in evidence, was the result of what you may think to have been a singularly 'sporting' wager. Haddock bet Vine £1,000 that his book *Forty Years of Fun* would sell five thousand copies. In fact, it sold many more than that. Vine paid up like a man, and the payment, of course, being a betting payment, was free of income tax.

It does not appear that the bookmaking side of Lotwoods' business is very successful. The cheques paid out by Vine are generally large: the bets he wins are often small. But that may happen to anyone in the gambling business. At the end of the last financial year the business showed a loss: but that loss of course he is entitled to set off against the profits of the publishing business as any man who runs two businesses may do. Vine, it is said, hopes for better things in the current year, and, meanwhile, is borrowing money from the publishing side, with whom he is on good terms.

So far, you may think, the story does not disclose anything that calls for the attention of a criminal court. The Crown, however, say that here is a criminal conspiracy between Vine and Haddock, and Vine and other authors, to avoid payment of income tax. Let it be said, at once, that the avoidance of tax is not necessarily an offence or even wrong. The prisoner Haddock could avoid tax by ceasing to write at all: and so harsh is the treatment of authors that it would not be surprising if he did. But it would be no crime. And, if a man chooses to acquire money by betting (untaxed) rather than by hard work (taxed), that, again, is his own affair. Haddock, in the box, shyly admitted that, elated by winning a bet of £1,000 from Mr Vine, he waived his royalties on the first five thousand copies of *Forty Years of Fun*. The Attorney-General found something fishy in that. You may think, as the Court thinks, that it was a very generous gesture. At all events, Mr Haddock is not bound to accept the royalties due to him. If he chooses, he can write for fun and give his books away.

The Attorney-General : But, milord . . .

The Judge : I know, I know, Sir Anthony. To the Treasury, of course, any transaction that does not yield them a fat harvest is tainted : but that is not the law.

The Attorney-General painted a lurid picture of what may happen if the prisoners are acquitted. All sorts of firms, he said, film companies, theatrical managers, banks, will set up ancillary bookmakers' businesses and millions of pounds will go free of tax as winning bets. That may be. But it does not mean that the transactions we are considering are illegal. It may mean that the law requires amendment. That is the business of Parliament. It is our business – yours and mine – to administer the law as it stands. Consider your verdict.

The jury found the prisoners *Not Guilty*, and recommended a complimentary grant to them from the public funds.

13 June 1951

Notes : 1. See also *Board of Inland Revenue* v. *the Dean of Alnwich* (1952), H.L., where the defendant made a successful wager of £5,000 with the Ecclesiastical Commissioners that a certain number of persons would attend divine service at the Cathedral within a certain period. *Held* (Lord Moon dissenting) that the payment was not liable to tax, though it was proved that the defendant had waived certain emoluments.

2. Since this case, by the Act of 1960, all bookmakers must be registered and licensed. But the main requirement for the granting of an ordinary bookmaker's permit is general respectability and a particular record of punctuality in the settlement of wagers. Messrs Lotwood, it is thought, should have no trouble – unless a tax is levied on winning wagers; and of this the Treasury appears incapable. For years such winnings were declared untaxable on the ground that they were 'capital gains'; when the Capital Gains Tax came in they were declared untaxable because they were *not* capital gains. What fun our dear Treasury is!

The Dead Pronunciation

REX *v*. VENABLES AND OTHERS

EXTRAORDINARY confusion prevailed this morning in the Lord Chief Justice's Court when Mr Ambrose Wick applied for a writ of *certiorari* to issue to the Petty Sessional Bench of Chimney Magna.

Mr Wick, a young advocate appearing in the High Court for the first time, said:

My lord, in these proceedings I ask for a rule *neessee* of *kairtiorahree* . . .

The Lord Chief Justice : I beg your pardon?

Mr Wick : Kairtiorahree. I am going to submit, my lord, that an order of the Chimney Magna justices was *ooltrah weerayze* . . .

The Court : I hope you will do nothing of the sort, Mr Wick. What is all this about?

Mr Wick : My lord, under the Emergency Drainage Act, 1923, the magistrates have power to make an order *pro hahk weekay* as between the beneficial owner of any sewer, culvert or conndewit, and the *day yooray* tenant of the storm-water channel for the assessment, my lord, *pahree pahssoo* . . .

The Court : Are you a Welshman, Mr Wick?

Mr Wick : No, my lord.

The Court : Then why do you not make yourself more plain? What do you mean by '*ooltrah weerayze*' and '*day yooray*'? Are they patent medicines or foreign potentates? So far the Court has no idea to what your application is directed.

Mr Wick : My lord, *ooltrah weerayze* – 'beyond the powers' . . .

The Court : Can it be said that you have in mind the Latin expression *ultra vires*?

Mr Wick : No, my lord; I never heard that expression before. My lord, in my submission the order of the magistrate was *ooltrah weerayze* . . .

The Court: Stop! Listen, Mr Wick. The two groups of sounds last formed by you have no meaning for me, and I order you not to make use of them again. Proceed, please.

Mr Wick: If your lordship pleases.

Continuing, the young advocate outlined the facts which had led up to the magistrates' order:

Mr Pottle, the *day yooray* tenant of the storm-water channel, was *preemah fakiay* the beneficial . . .

The Court: Do you mean *prima facie*, Mr Wick?

Mr Wick: No, my lord – *preemah fakiay*.

The Court (after a moment's hesitation): Go on.

Mr Wick: And, my lord, as the *preemah fakiay* beneficial owner, he claimed by prescription the *yooss waynahndee et piscahndee* over the upper waters of the Float River, which issued through the conndewit . . .

The Court: Nullum tempus occurrit regi, Mr Wick.

Mr Wick: I beg your lordship's pardon?

The Court: Nullum tempus occurrit regi.

Mr Wick: With great respect, my lord, I don't quite understand.

The Court: Oh, my sacred aunt! Would you understand if I said '*Nooloom tempooss okkooreet raygee*'?

Mr Wick (with a happy smile): Perfectly, milord – perfectly. I am very grateful to your lordship. My lord I was coming to that point. But, my lord, Mr Pottle, summoned before the magistrates upon *soob poynah* . . .

The Court: Soob what?

Mr Wick: Soob poynah, my lord.

The Court: Do you mean that he was *sub-poenaed*?

Mr Wick: No, my lord.

The Court: Mr Wick, I am sorry, but this is not to be endured. I should be reluctant to think that you were treating the Court with levity . . .

Mr Wick: My *lord* – indeed, no! *Noan possoomooss.*

The Court: Do not break into Latin again, Mr Wick. I take it that you have but recently concluded your education and that this is the first appearance in the King's Courts of what is called, or *was* called, the New Pronunciation of Latin . . .

Mr Wick: My lord, I pronounce the Latin tongue as I was taught at school.

The Lord Chief Justice: Exactly. You are not to be blamed, Mr Wick. But I am bound to make it clear to you, to the rest of your gallant generation and to the generations that come after, that His Majesty's judges will not permit the speaking of the Latin tongue after that fashion in the King's Courts. I cannot hear you, Mr Wick, for the very good reason that I cannot understand you. We are using different languages. It might be possible to establish communication between us by the use of an interpreter. I see no necessity for that expensive and protracted process, though I am tempted to compel the attendance of one of your pastors and masters to discharge the office of interpreter and witness the unhappy plight to which they have brought you. It is not for me at my time of life to learn a new language; it is not for the King's judges to remodel their diction according to the whims of pedagogues or the habits of the Junior Bar. The bitter conclusion is, Mr Wick, that you must go away and learn to pronounce the Latin tongue correctly, according to the immemorial practice of your profession.

I hope that these observations will be communicated by you to the particular pedagogues responsible for your predicament and by the newspapers to the general world of education. It may have been hoped in the schools that by catching and corrupting a few generations of the young it would be possible to force this lisping, hybrid, artificial baby-talk upon the learned professions. That hope must have been moribund for many years, and it gives me pleasure now to sign its certificate of death.

In the legal profession, above all others, the Latin tongue is a living force, a priceless aid to precision of thought, to verbal economy and practical efficiency. Any knowing business man who mocks the study of the 'dead' languages has only to sit in our Courts for an hour or two to learn how very far from dead the Latin language is; and if he still regards its use as the elegant foible of a number of old fogies I hope that he will try to translate into a few brief businesslike words such common phrases as *a priori, de jure, ultra vires, ex parte, status quo* and many others. We have taken these words from Rome, as we have taken much of her law, and made them English. I do not believe that the wisest scholars can surely say how Julius Caesar pronounced his name, and I care nothing if they can. For if I had abundant proof that the general answered to Yooliooss Kayzar I should not be persuaded to say that an act of the Chimney Magna justices was *ooltrah weerayze*. It is safe to prophesy that these hateful sounds will never proceed from the lips of an English judge, however many innocent boys are instructed to make them at school.

The same may be said of all the professions in which the 'dead' languages are not merely the toys of pedagogues but the constant tools of practical men. I suffer from lumbago; I grow geraniums; I go to the cinema. And when my doctor diagnoses loombahgo, my gardener cultivates gerahniooms, or my cook enjoys herself at the kyneemah I shall begin to think that the pedagogues are making headway.

As for the political world, the numerous Latin words in current political usage are sufficiently mystifying to the man-in-the-tavern without our attempting to make him pronounce them as some good don believes they might have been pronounced by Cicero or Horace. Even the mocking business man is not ashamed to draw his dividends at so much *per centum*; but not all the pedants of Arabia will induce him to draw them *pair kentoom*.

It follows, I think, that a system of teaching Latin which runs contrary to the practical use of Latin wherever Latin is practically employed is wrong and ought to be abandoned. This has been said before; but it is time for it to be said by one of His Majesty's judges. For our profession more than any other employs the naked Latin word as it was written by the Romans; and we alone are in a position to enforce our will upon this matter by guiding the speech of those who practise before us.

Mr Wick, I am sorry for you. I look forward to seeing you before me again, cured of the horrid habits your professors taught you, and able to take that place in the ranks of your profession which your talents evidently deserve. Meanwhile, through your unhappy person, I issue, in the name of His Majesty's judges, this edict to the educationists ('What,' as Mr Haddock has so ably said, 'a word!'): The New Pronunciation is dead and must be buried.

The Court rose.

31 January 1934

Wear and Tear

HADDOCK AND OTHERS *v.* BOARD OF INLAND REVENUE

THIS was an appeal from a decision of the Income Tax Commissioners to the High Court.

Mr Justice Radish : The appellant in this case is a Mr Albert Haddock, a pertinacious litigant whom we are always glad to see. And let me say that it gives me pleasure to see the Commissioners, so often and for such poor cause the initiators of litigation, for once upon their defence.

Mr Haddock asks for a declaration that he is, and has been for some years, entitled to certain allowances or deductions for income tax purposes under the heading of (*a*) Expenses and (*b*) Wear and Tear of Machinery and Plant; and on the assumption that he is right he claims that a considerable sum is owing to him in respect of past years in which the Commissioners have refused to grant him such allowances.

Mr Haddock appears on behalf of the whole body of authors, artists, and composers, and the position of a large number of creative brain-workers will be affected by our decision.

Now the theory of Income Tax (under Schedule D) is that it is a tax upon the *profits* of occupations, professions, or businesses. The manufacturer of soap, who makes and sells soap to the value of ten thousand pounds, at a cost to himself of eight thousand pounds, is taxed upon two thousand pounds. If there is no profit there is (in theory) no tax. He is not taxed on what comes into the till, but upon what goes into the savings bank. Further, it is recognized by the State that his soap-manufacturing machinery and plant must in the nature of things suffer wear and tear with the passage of time, and on account of that depreciation he is allowed to deduct certain sums from his income, apart from the day-to-day expenses of his business.

The position of the author, artist, or composer is very different. But it is Mr Haddock's first complaint that the

Commissioners treat him as if he were in the same position as the soap-manufacturer, except where it would benefit him to be treated so. In the vulgar phrase, he says, they have it both ways. The author is taxed, practically speaking, not on profits but on *receipts*, on almost everything that comes into the till. For the small deductions allowed to him on account of professional expenses are meagre and in no way comparable to the expenses side of the soap-manufacturer's profit-and-loss accounts.

An author, says Mr Haddock, cannot write about nothing (though one or two come very near to it). The whole of life is his raw material, and, like other raw material, it has to be paid for. His friendships, love-affairs, marriages, journeys, sports, reading, recreation, and social relations cannot be had for nothing. Mr Haddock argues very plausibly that his expenditure on these items, without which he would be unable to carry on his profession at all, should be entered on the 'loss' side of his profit-and-loss account. The Commissioners, however, have obstinately refused to allow him anything by way of expenses, except for such obvious and trivial items as stationery, typewriting, use of secretary, pens, pencils, indiarubber, and so forth; they have allowed him nothing for hospitality, entertainment, or travel, and they have invariably deleted from his list of professional expenses such items as champagne, Monte Carlo, night-club subscriptions, 'first-nights', Deauville, and hire of yacht at Cowes. 'But how,' says Mr Haddock, 'can a man write about Monte Carlo or Cowes unless he goes to Monte Carlo or Cowes? How is he to study and depict the gilded life of Society without constant visits to the Saveloy Grill Room, to Covent Garden, to the Riviera, and other places where Society is to be found?' These questions seem to me to be unanswerable; and they received no satisfactory answer from the representative of the defendants in the box. Further, it is not denied that if a soap-manufacturer were compelled for business reasons to visit Cowes or Monte Carlo he would be permitted to deduct the necessary expenses of the expedition when calculating his taxable income. I see no reason why Mr Haddock should not do the same.

Next, as to wear and tear. One of the constant disadvantages of the author's trade is that he is a one-man business, at once his own employer, designer, technician, machine-minder, and machine. Once the soap-manufacturer has equipped and organized his factory he may relax; a week's holiday, a month's illness will not suspend the output of his soap or the growth of his income. But when the author stops the machine stops and the output stops. He is unable, on holidays, in sickness, or in age, to depute his functions to any other person. Here is one more reason why a hundred pounds earned by the author should not be treated and taxed on the same terms as a hundred pounds accruing as profit to the soap-manufacturer. 'Yet,' says Mr Haddock, 'since this is done, let it be done thoroughly and logically. The author's machinery and plant are his brain and his physique, his fund of inventiveness, his creative powers. These are not inexhaustible; they are seldom rested (for the reasons given above); the strain upon them increases as the years go by, and in some cases, I understand, is aggravated by late hours and dissipation. If it is proper for the soap-manufacturer to be relieved in respect of the wear and tear of his machinery and the renewal thereof (which money can easily buy), how much more consideration is owing to the delicate and irreplaceable mechanism of the writer!'

Under this head Mr Haddock has repeatedly appealed for relief in respect of sums expended on doctor's accounts, on sunlight treatment, on nourishing foods and champagne, and upon necessary holidays at Monte Carlo and Cowes. The Commissioners have refused, and I find that they were wrong.

Under both heads, therefore, Mr Haddock's appeal succeeds. He estimates that if his expenses be properly calculated on the basis already explained he has never yet made a taxable profit; for at the end of every year of his literary operations he has been a little more in debt than the year before. In every year, therefore, he has been wrongly assessed and unlawfully taxed; and I order the Commissioners to reopen the accounts for the past seven years and repay to Mr Haddock the very large sums owing to him.

I may add a few words for the general guidance of Inland Revenue officials in this class of case. There seems to be a

notion abroad (especially in Parliament, where every erroneous
notion is carefully incubated) that the author deserves less
generous treatment than the soap-manufacturer, on the ground
that the latter is an employer of labour. Mr Haddock in his
evidence, some of which I read with reluctance, has ably exposed the fallacy herein contained, though his observations on
the Derating Act were perhaps tinged with irrelevance. 'It is
difficult,' he said, 'to discuss this notion with patience. What a
poop Parliament is, milord! The authors, writers, and composers are in a sense the biggest employers in the country, for
they are the only original creators of employment. Their books,
their articles, their music must be typed and printed and bound
and distributed, performed upon the stage, the wireless, the
gramophone, and the screen. The publishers, printers, com-
positors, bookbinders, and booksellers, the actors, musicians,
singers, and stage-hands – nay, the very newspaper proprietors
and their enormous staffs, owe their employment, their earnings, and their profits to the creative mind and technical skill
of the writer, since without him their occupation would be
nothing and their machines be silent. He is the producer and
they an army of middlemen; he is the true creator of wealth,
and they, if I may employ the genial language of a certain
political party, are but parasites upon his brains and labour.
Yet Parliament, in its recent Derating Act, designed to encourage and increase employment, extends the privileges of
that Act to the printer and not to the author who finds employment for that printer, 'derates' the 'factory' section of a
newspaper office, but not the editorial side, without which that
factory would be idle and valueless. My lord, how character-
istically crass of Parliament! How utterly soggy! How . . .'
But perhaps Mr Haddock's point is now clear enough. The
question whether the premises of authors ought to be classed as
'factories' must be decided by some other tribunal. But the
principles laid down by Mr Haddock for the proper estimation
of authors and writers are sound, and should govern the Commissioners in all their dealings with this deserving and valuable
class of men. The appeal is allowed.

30 July 1930

Why is the Coroner?

TRISTRAM *v*. THE MOON LIFE ASSURANCE COMPANY

(*Before Mr Justice Oat*)

STRONG comments on the conduct of a coroner were made by the learned judge in his summing-up to the jury in this case today.

His Lordship : Lord Mildew remarked in a famous case, the name of which I forget : 'It is the duty of coroners to investigate the death of the deceased and not, as some of them seem to think, the lives of the living. Even an inquest can be too inquisitive.' It is a pity that that dictum has never been brought to the attention of Dr Busy, the Bathbourne Coroner. The office of coroner is ancient, odd, anomalous, and perhaps unnecessary.[1] It is of interest to note that as far back as the thirteenth century the coroner had gained a reputation for interfering in matters which did not properly concern him. In Magna Carta it was thought worth while to include a chapter restraining his activities, and this was later re-enacted in the Coroners' Act of 1887.

It is a commonplace that the majority of men seem to have more importance at the time of death than they have ever had before; the whole nation may become agitated about the tragic death of some unfortunate fellow to whom nobody gave a thought so long as he was alive. And some of this factitious importance appears to attach itself to the coroner, who, having to deal with the dead from time to time, makes more stir in the world than those officers of the law who have to deal with the living six days in the week.

By the strange provisions of the Coroners Amendment Act, 1926, a coroner must be either a solicitor, a barrister, or a legally qualified medical practitioner of five years' standing in

1. He is not found necessary, for example, in Scotland.

his profession. And legally qualified, I understand, does not mean, as many suppose, a doctor who has made some study of the law. It means no more than a medical practitioner lawfully qualified to be a doctor.[1] I have never understood why, if it was necessary or desirable to go outside the ranks of the legal profession for coroners, a medical man was considered to be the only possible alternative. The doctor, so far as I know, is no better qualified to exercise judicial functions than the banker, the business man, the civil servant, landowner, soldier, sailor, or schoolmaster. Indeed, *a priori*, much as I admire the medical profession, there are good reasons for thinking the contrary.

The doctor is accustomed by training and habit to found strong theories upon circumstantial evidence, and is often compelled by the necessity for immediate action to frame a firm diagnosis at a stage when the evidence is necessarily incomplete. And once he has adopted a certain hypothesis it is extremely difficult to persuade him to abandon it. Once my dear doctor has pronounced that I have mumps or whooping-cough I have mumps or whooping-cough. A 'second opinion' may ultimately show that I have, in fact, some glandular affection or tropical disease. But the taking of a 'second opinion', as you know, is a rare proceeding, only consented to in cases of exceptional doubt or difficulty. This apparent self-confidence is without doubt a valuable part of the technique of the medical world, where the patient's belief in the infallibility of his adviser is often an essential contributor to his recovery.

But in the legal profession we do not pretend to be quite so clever. The splendid pyramid of our appeal tribunals has been erected upon the generous assumption that the judge and the lawyer are as liable to error as those whom they advise or condemn. We are always taking 'second opinions', and scarcely any of us can make a move without one. Before the writ is issued the solicitor consults a barrister, and after it is issued the barrister consults the solicitor. The judge consults the clerk of the Court, the Bar, the precedents, the jury, and even the Acts of Parliament; and when with all those aids he has arrived at a

1. This was erroneous. See Note.

decision he is cheerfully prepared for the litigant to take a 'second opinion' from the Court of Appeal. Of all the numerous tribunals in the land, only the House of Lords and the Judicial Committee of the Privy Council are deemed so likely to be right that no appeal can go beyond them; and even then it cannot be said that any one man has the last word, since the decision is made by the majority of three judges or more, each of whom has the opportunity to take a 'second opinion' from each of the others.

The only one-man judicial tribunal whose pronouncements are never, in practice, subjected to a 'second opinion' is the coroner. The High Court has power, both at Common Law and by statute, to quash a coroner's inquisition and order a new one.[1] But these powers are rarely used and do not cover the whole mischief.

There are three dangers: (1) that by reason of the coroner's queer proceedings a person may wrongly be accused of crime; (2) that a person properly accused and tried may be unjustly hampered and endangered by a cloud of inquest-generated prejudice; and (3) that, without being tried, wholly innocent persons, witnesses or relatives, may be blackened with coroner's mud. The High Court's powers may avail in an extreme case of (1) but rarely in (2), and never in (3), for the mischief is done. Moreover, the coroner may do much damage without doing anything of which the High Court could properly take notice.

A judge may err, may even be tempted, from time to time, into irrelevant and unjust censure. But he is bound by rules and traditions, and is always aware of the possibility that his proceedings may be reviewed and reversed by a superior Court. The coroner is not.

In short, the doctor, as such, has been selected for the one judicial post where an autocratic habit of mind is likely to be most dangerous, because it is in effect an autocratic office.

To come to the present case, Mr Reginald Tristram was found dead in his pyjamas underneath his bedroom window. He was a sleep-walker, as you have heard. But the coroner's

1. There was such a case in 1930.

jury, strongly directed by Dr Ambrose Busy, brought in a
verdict of *felo de se*. The effect of this was not only to cause pain
and grief to his relatives and to deny to the deceased the rites of
Christian burial. A clause in the policy of insurance on the
life of the deceased made the policy void in the event of suicide:
the insurance company have denied liability, and this action
is the result.

Now, a finding of fact by a coroner's inquisition is not in law
binding on anyone, although in practice, as I have said, it may
have permanent effects. 'Mud sticks,' as Lord Mildew said in
Boot v. *The Ecclesiastical Commissioners*. Nor is it even *prima
facie* evidence of the cause of death (see *Bird* v. *Keep* (1918),
2 K.B.) in an action which turns upon the cause of death.
This Court has to consider the question whether the deceased
committed suicide or not, as if it had never been considered
by the coroner at all. (Which, by the way, is an interesting
commentary on the airs which Dr Busy gives himself.)

I therefore, as you heard, directed both sides that the
coroner's proceedings were not even to be mentioned. I have
gone out of my way to mention them myself – first, because I
desired to express my detestation of Dr Busy, and secondly,
because, if he had conducted the inquiry properly, this action,
in my view, need never have been brought, and it is the duty of
the Courts to discourage unnecessary litigation. *Interest
reipublicae ut sit finis litium*.

Acting upon this principle, I am now going to read to you
an extract from the report of the proceedings at Dr Busy's
inquiry. There is one habit common among medical men which
I have not mentioned: the habit of asking a great many questions not immediately concerned with the matter in hand. While
our dear doctor is making up his mind whether we are suffering
from mumps or meningitis, typhoid fever or incipient pneu-
monia, he will put to us all manner of inquiries about our recent
behaviour, our diet, our bowels, our dreams, drinks, recrea-
tions, and professional cares. Unexpected clues may from time to
time be stumbled upon in this way. On the other hand, the process
enables the questioner to appear most knowing when he is in
fact in the most profound perplexity. An innocent and even

helpful practice in the examination of the patient; and we can understand the inclination of a doctor to use the same technique for the investigation of truth in court. But what is proper for the private consulting-room may be most improper at a public inquest. Dr Busy seems to treat his witnesses as if they were panel-patients endeavouring to conceal from him the origins of some discreditable disease. British justice assumes that all those who come into court are innocent until the contrary is shown. Dr Busy, by professional habit, assumes that all those who come before him have something wrong with them, and that it is his business to put them right.

The Coroner: What time was it when you say you found the body of your father?

George Tristram (22): As I approached the house I heard the clock strike two.

Coroner: Why were you returning home at two o'clock in the morning?

Witness: What has that got to do with it?

Coroner (sternly): Answer the question, sir. It is my duty to elicit the truth.

Witness: About my father's death, yes, sir, but not about my evening out.

Coroner: So you had had an 'evening out'? Were you sober?

Witness: Yes. I'd been out to supper. Dancing. You can't dance drunk.

Coroner: You had been out to supper. With a woman?

Witness: Of course. Do you suppose I should dance with a leopard?

Coroner: No impertinence, please. What is the woman's name?

Witness: Mind your own business.

Coroner: At this moment, sir, it is my duty to mind yours. I must ask you for the woman's name.

Witness: Pratt.

Coroner: Miss or Mrs?

Witness: Mrs.

The Coroner here ordered Mrs Pratt to be sent for.

Coroner: So you were having an evening out with a married woman? Was her husband aware of this?

Witness: Really, sir, what has all this got to do with . . .

Coroner: Answer the question.

Witness: Probably not.

Coroner: Probably not. You mean that you and this woman are deceiving the husband?

Witness: No, I don't. I mean they don't live together any more.

Coroner: Divorced?

Witness: Practically.

Coroner: Practically divorced. Then the husband has obtained a decree *nisi*?

Witness: No, you fool! *She* has.

Coroner: Oh! So you returned home at two a.m. after dancing with a successful petitioner for divorce whose decree has not been made absolute?

The Coroner here ordered his officer to communicate with the King's Proctor.

Coroner: Is this the Mr Pratt who went bankrupt not long ago?

And so on. There was in this case no question of murder or manslaughter. The simple question was: 'Did the deceased fall out of the window by accident or on purpose?' But in his blundering search for an answer Dr Busy succeeded in blackening the character of every member of the bereaved family and four of their friends. He probed the secrets of their private lives as if he were searching their intestines for a needle. Their resentment of his impertinence inflamed his suspicions; he formed the fantastic theory that they were a family of rakes who by their loose behaviour had driven the deceased to self-destruction; and this theory he impressed upon the jury.

In my judgment the medical profession in general and Dr Busy in particular are not well qualified for the discharge of judicial functions. I may add that I think the office of coroner should be abolished, and the civilized practice of Scotland adopted in this country.

In Scotland, as I understand the matter, the preliminary inquiries into the cause of a violent or suspicious death are conducted *in private* by the police and the Procurator Fiscal (the local Public Prosecutor), who consults, if necessary, the Law Officers or their trained assistants. If they decide that there ought to be a public trial there is *one* public trial, not two: and a man suspected of murder will not come to that trial in the cloud of prejudice with which the crude procedure and publicity of our inquest system surrounds him. If the coroner's office must be retained it should be entrusted only to trained lawyers observing a strict and uniform code of procedure. We will now consider the case before us.

31 May, 1933

Note: Thirty-three years later, in June 1966, the Council of the Law Society, replying to questions from the Home Office, said: 'The Council consider that the appropriate qualification for a coroner is a legal one, since a legal training provides a more adequate qualification for presiding over an inquiry than does a medical training.'

But the aged Mr Justice Oat was wrong about the recent Act. A doctor-coroner must be nominally a lawyer but need not have practised. The Council think that a coroner should have had 'five years active practice' of the law.

Fish Royal

(Before Mr Justice Wool)

IN this unusual action, the hearing of which was begun today, an interesting point is raised concerning the rights and duties of the Crown in connexion with a dead whale.

Sir Ethelred Rutt, K.C. (for the plaintiffs): May it please your lordship, this action is brought by Mr Tinrib, Mr Rumble, and the other plaintiffs on behalf of the inhabitants of Pudding Magna, situated, milord, in the county of Dorset . . .

The Court: Where is Dorset?

Sir Ethelred: Milord, I have a map here. Dorset, milord, if your lordship will glance at the bottom left-hand corner . . . Dorset, milord, is, milord, Dorset . . .

The Court: Quite, quite. Get on, please, Sir Ethelred.

Sir Ethelred: I am greatly obliged to your lordship. Pudding Magna, milord, is situated in the north-east corner of Pudding Bay, or the Devil's Entry. The inhabitants are mainly fisher-folk of lowly origin and modest means, and, so far as can be ascertained, the place is not referred to in any of the works of Mr Thomas Hardy, Mr William Wordsworth, or any other writer . . .

The Court: O si sic omnes!

Sir Ethelred: Ha! Milord, in the night of 21 June last a dead whale was washed up on the shore of Pudding Bay, at a point south-west by south from the township of Pudding Magna. Now, the whale, milord, together with the sturgeon and the swan, is Fish Royal, and belongs to the King; or, to be precise, the head of the whale belongs to His Majesty the King and the tail to Her Majesty the Queen. Your lordship will recall the case of *Rex* v. *Monday* (1841) 3 A.C., which decided the latter point.

The Court: I recall nothing of the kind.

Sir Ethelred: Your lordship is very good. The loyal inhabitants of Pudding Magna, milord, made haste to extract from the carcass of the whale the whalebone, the blubber, and other valuable and perishable portions, with the intention, I am instructed, of holding them in trust for the Crown. And I may say at once that any other construction of their motives will be most strenuously resisted, if necessary, by sworn evidence. Three days later, milord, the wind, which had been northerly, shifted to the prevailing quarter, which is south-east . . .

Sir Wilfred Knocknee, K.C.: You mean south-west.

Sir Ethelred: I am very greatly obliged to me learned friend. Me learned friend is perfectly right, milord; the prevailing wind is south-west, milord; and, milord, on the fifth day the presence of the whale began to be offensive to the inhabitants of Pudding Magna. They therefore looked with confidence to the Crown to remove to a more convenient place the remnants of the Crown's property . . .

Sir Wilfred (aside): For which they had no use.

Sir Ethelred: Really, milord, me learned friend must not whisper insinuations of that kind under his breath; really, milord, I am entitled to resent, milord . . .

The Court: Go on, Sir Ethelred.

Sir Ethelred: Your lordship is extraordinarily handsome and good. Accordingly, milord, the Mayor of Pudding Magna addressed a humble petition to the Home Secretary, milord, begging him to acquaint His Majesty with the arrival of his property and praying for its instant removal. And by a happy afterthought, milord, a copy of this petition was sent to the Minister of Agriculture and Fisheries.

Happy, milord, for this reason, that the original communication appears to have escaped the notice of the Home Secretary entirely. At the Ministry of Agriculture and Fisheries, however, the Mayor's letter was handed to a public servant named Sleep, a newcomer to the Service, and one, it seems, who combined with a fertile imagination an unusual incapacity for the conduct of practical affairs. This gentleman has now left the public service, milord, and will be called.

It appears, milord, that, when the Mayor's letter had been lying unconsidered on Mr Sleep's desk for several days, the following telegram was handed to him:

To the King London whale referred to in previous communications now in advanced stages decomposition humbly petition prompt action

Tinrib

Mr Sleep, milord, according to his own account, turning the matter over in his sagacious mind, at once hit upon a solution which would be likely to satisfy the requirements of His Majesty's Treasury with regard to public economy. Two days later, therefore, a letter was addressed to the Director of the Natural History Museum informing him that an unusually fine specimen of *Balaena Biscayensis* was now lying in Pudding Bay and that the Minister was authorized by His Majesty to offer the whale to the Museum in trust for the nation, the Museum to bear the charges of collection and transport.

On 3 July, milord, the Secretary to the Natural History Museum replied that he was desired by the Director to express his regret that, owing to lack of space, the Museum was unable to accept His Majesty's gracious offer. He was to add that the Museum was already in possession of three fine specimens of *Balaena Biscayensis*.

Milord, for some days, it appears, Mr Sleep took no further action. Meanwhile, milord, the whale had passed from the advanced to the penultimate stages of decomposition, and had begun to poison the sea at high water, thereby gravely impairing the fishermen's livelihood. Mr Tinrib, milord, was in constant, but one-sided, correspondence with Mr Sleep; and on the 12th of July, milord, Mr Sleep lunched with a friend and colleague at the Admiralty, Mr Sloe. While they were engaged, milord, upon the discussion of fish, the topic of whales naturally arose, and Mr Sleep, milord, unofficially, milord, expressed to Mr Sloe the opinion that the Ministry of Agriculture and Fisheries would be willing to grant to the Admiralty the use of the whale for the purpose of target-practice; and he suggested that one of His Majesty's ships should be immediately detailed to tow His Majesty's whale out to sea. He also pointed out the peculiar advantages of such a target for the exercise of such vessels as were called upon to fire at submarines. Mr Sloe, milord, undertook to explore the opinion of the Admiralty on the proposal, and the conference broke up.

That was on the 12th. On the 17th, milord, Mr Sloe unofficially, milord, at a further lunch, intimated to Mr Sleep that he could find no support among their Lordships of the Admiralty for the proposal of the Ministry of Agriculture and Fisheries; for, while excellent practice was to be had from a disappearing target, their Lordships could not sanction the expenditure of ammunition on a target which must, at most ranges, be quite invisible. Further, it was their opinion that by the date of the autumn firing-practices the whale would have suffered dissolution by the ordinary processes of nature.

The inhabitants of Pudding Magna, milord, did not share this view. On the 20th, milord, Mr Tinrib and a deputation waited upon Mr Sleep. They pointed out to Mr Sleep that all fishing was suspended in Pudding Bay; that Pudding Magna was now scarcely habitable except on the rare occasions of a northerly wind; that the majority of the citizens had fled to the hills and were living in huts and caves. They further inquired, milord, whether it would be lawful for the fishermen themselves to destroy the whale, so far as that could be done, with explosives, and, if so, whether the Crown would refund the cost of the explosives, which might be considerable. As to this, milord, Mr Sleep was unable to accept the responsibility of expressing an opinion; but the whale was undoubtedly Crown property, and he questioned gravely whether the Treasury would sanction the expenditure of public money on the destruction of Crown property by private citizens. He also pointed out that the Treasury, if approached, would be likely to require a strict account of any whalebone, blubber, and other material extracted from the whale's carcass. Mention of explosives however, had suggested to his mind that possibly the War Office might be interested in the whale, and he undertook to inquire. The deputation agreed, milord, that this perhaps would be the better course, and withdrew.

On the 24th, milord, a letter was dispatched to the War Office pointing out that the whale now lying in Pudding Bay offered excellent opportunities for the training of engineers in the removal of obstacles, and could well be made the centre of any amphibious operations, landing-parties, invasions, etc., which might form part of the forthcoming manoeuvres. The War Office would doubtless take note of the convenient proximity of the whale to the Tank Corps Depot at Lulworth.

On the 31st, milord, the War Office replied that the destruction of whales by tanks was no longer considered a practicable operation of war, and that no part of the forthcoming manoeuvres would be amphibious.

From this date, milord, Mr Sleep seems to have abandoned his efforts. At any rate, on the 4th of August, Mr Tinrib received the following evasive and disgraceful communication:

WHALE, CARCASS OF

Dear Sir,
'I am desired by the Minister of Agriculture and Fisheries to observe that your representations to this Department appear to have been made under a misapprehension. It should hardly be necessary to state that the whale is not a fish but a mammal. I am therefore to express regret that the Ministry of Agriculture and Fisheries can accept no responsibility in the matter.

In these circumstances, milord, the inhabitants, or I should say the *late* inhabitants, of Pudding Magna have been compelled to institute these proceedings, and humbly pray . . .

The case was adjourned.

1 October 1924

No Taxation without Representation

BOARD OF INLAND REVENUE *v.* HADDOCK

(*Before Mr Justice Plush*)

HIS LORDSHIP, giving judgment said:

In this case the Court is required to consider once again the tiresome objections of Mr Albert Haddock to the taxes on toil which the rest of the citizens so much enjoy or, at the least, contentedly endure. But however deficient the defendant may be in patriotism or, if you will, in twentieth-century servility, we must control our loathing and consider his plea, if there is reason in it. After many courteous and kindly representations from the Special Commissioners for Income Tax, Mr Haddock has declined to pay the surtax due from him for the year 1952–3. The surtax only: the income tax on his earnings for the same period, says the defendant, he has reluctantly but cheerfully paid. The surtax is another matter. The income tax is a burden shared by all the Queen's subjects, not equally, it is true, but in a roughly equitable relation to their earnings or possessions. The surtax is a punitive levy, almost a fine, upon those citizens who by special industry, ability, or fortune earn money above a figure fixed by Governments and Parliaments as the pardonable peak of personal incomes.

The figure, at present, is £2,000, so that Her Majesty's Judges, as well as the defendant, may count themselves among the criminal classes. This tax is exacted not one year (like the income tax) but two years after the relevant earnings have been received and enjoyed. In 1952, the defendant told us, by exceptional toil and merit, he achieved a rare success in his precarious profession. In 1953 he yielded by way of income tax more than half of his reward. After such a transaction the most earnest patriot might well suppose that he would be left in peace to enjoy what was left of the fruits of his labours. But no, in 1954 down comes the State again with a second demand for surtax on the same earnings: and the two exactions, over a certain area, amounted to as much as nineteen shillings in the pound. 'Not,' said the defendant dryly, 'a great encouragement to imaginative effort.' This double, or delayed, punishment provoked Mr Haddock, in cross-examination, to a vivid though disrespectful figure of speech. 'The Treasury,' he said, 'is like the barracuda.'

Question 2539. *Sir Anthony Slatt:* Why the barracuda, Mr Haddock?

Answer: The shark takes one of your legs and goes away. The barracuda comes back and takes the other one.

We must give the defendant his due; and in this case he has not wearied the Court with his usual assaults on the entire structure and practice of contemporary taxation, the avarice, extravagance and incompetence of the State, and the particular hazards or sufferings of his own profession. He is concerned, it appears, for all those who are required to pay surtax, and indeed is the Founder, President, and Secretary of a body called the Surtax Rebellion League. This association, in spite of its title, is said to be based upon strict constitutional principles. The motto surrounding its crest (an odd portrait of the Founder shaking one fist and scribbling with the other) is 'No Taxation Without Representation'. These are words that strike a gong in the breast of every Briton, words of the same high quality and standing as 'No arrest without trial' or 'Grievances before supply'. I was going to add 'One Man, One Vote': but the defendant has reminded us that that is, comparatively, a modern saying, and a practice still to be approved by history. Far back in 1765 that great lawyer the Earl of Camden, Attorney-General, Chief Justice, and then Lord Chancellor, said in the House of Lords:

The British Parliament has no right to tax the Americans . . . Taxation and representation are inseparably united. God hath joined them: no British Parliament can put them asunder. To endeavour to do so is to stab our very vitals.

That fine principle is still respected, up to a point, in our political affairs. The representatives of the people in Parliament have an opportunity to criticize, to vote against, the taxes, and if their grievances are not redressed, to refuse supply. But, say the defendant and his friends, there is no longer the same link between taxation and representation as our fathers had in mind, for the simple reason that all the people do not pay the same taxes, and those that pay the least are more generously represented than those that pay the most.

It is idle, then, says the defendant, to pretend that they are equally represented. If the incidence of income tax upon labourers and artisans is in debate, they can be sure, because of their numbers, that their interests will be duly considered and protected. Every Member of Parliament, after all, has to suffer the same tax. But can the few selected for the surtax expect the same consideration? It is good, without a doubt, that every man and woman should have a part in the government of the country, that all should have a vote. It may be true that the young man who has successfully reached the age of twenty-one, and has resided in the same borough for three months, is as well able to pronounce upon the complicated affairs of the modern world, as well fitted to choose a government, as the head of a bank, a business, or college, a scientist, doctor, man of letters, or High Court judge. That is one thing, says the defendant. But it is quite another to give them equal weapons in the arena of taxation. In other words, he boldly – impiously, some will say – attacks the principle of One Man, One Vote. All, he says, should have at least one vote: but for every £500 of £1,000 that he pays in direct taxation he should receive another vote at the next General Election on presenting the proper certificates to the Returning Officer. The Court observed that, after a long Parliament, many high and hard-working citizens would have perhaps twenty or thirty votes. The defendant, unabashed, replied (Q. 3103):

Certainly. Why not? They would then receive more attention in Parliament, and the 'marriage' between taxation and representation of which Lord Camden spoke would be restored.

In the absence of such arrangements the Court is asked to

declare that the surtax is unconstitutional and need not be paid. Not for the first time, I have come to the conclusion that there is something in what Mr Haddock says – but not enough. I agree that this is a brutal and shameful tax, contrary to natural justice and ancient principles of the Constitution: but the sovereign Parliament has feebly consented to it and there it is. Mr Haddock must pay, if he can – this time.

But there may be other remedies. In the box, when cross-examined on the aims of the League, he incautiously mentioned the possibility of a surtax strike. The annual yield of this odious and unjust levy, we were told, is about £130,000,000, which even in these fantastic days may be counted as an important sum. If all the surtax victims decided at once to withhold their earnings, as the labourers, from time to time, 'withhold their labour', the Exchequer would be gravely embarrassed, and it would not be so easy to proceed against many as it is against one. But though this is not a criminal court, I may offer the defendant a friendly warning. His League has not the glorious standing of a Trade Union, and so is not above the ordinary law. If, in such an event as he has imagined, there were any evidence of organization or incitement, he might well find himself in the dock on a criminal charge of conspiracy. But if there were some sort of spontaneous combustion, if all the surtaxees – each on his own – decided suddenly that their injustices were no longer to be borne, no charge of conspiracy could arise.

But let us be careful, Mr Haddock. I should not advise anyone to strike, in terms, against the tax itself: for, in these envious days, he could not be sure of the sympathy of the people or the papers. No, no; the labourers, in these days, frequently take 'industrial action' about matters with which they do not seem to be very closely concerned – foreign policy, the sale of Government aeroplanes, the affairs of Trade Unions to which they do not belong, the employment of labourers who do not belong to their own, and this and that. Let every sur-tax-striker have a political purpose of his own. One will protest against the treacherous abolition of the University seats, another against the feeble failure to restore them, one against the

Rule of Noise, another against the persecution of the Pools, and so on. Every man will do the same thing on the same date, for a different reason. How about 1st January 1955, Mr Haddock? Would that be convenient, do you think, to us all?

Mr Haddock: Certainly, my Lord.

The Court: Very well. I will send you my subscription to the League. Meanwhile, in this case, the plaintiffs must succeed. But the plaintiffs – curse them! – will jolly well pay the costs.

14 July 1954

Note: Your editor, perhaps, was the only man living who followed the same line of thought on the transition of many African States from a colonial status to independence. During the Rhodesian controversy of 1965–6 the leader of another African State said that the only basis of true democracy was 'One Man,–One Vote'. Your editor remarked that even in Britain this absurd and arid formula was only fifteen to sixteen years old, and in Africa it had as much virtue as 'One Man, One Baby'. Britain has been a democracy for many years, but the first Parliament strictly elected by 'One Man, One Vote' was the Parliament of 1950: before that there had been the business vote and the university vote, both easily defensible as ingredients of good government. By some administrative slip no one consulted me about the constitutions of Rhodesia or any of the new independencies. I should have said: By all means give every man *one* vote. But let him be able to win more than one, by showing merit and acquiring responsibility – by passing examinations, winning public appointments, by long or distinguished service in the forces, by success in agriculture or industry (which is easily shown by his earnings or his taxes). 'One Man, One Vote' is justifiable only in a State where all men are equally wise, virtuous, and useful. 'One Man, One Baby' would be equally impracticable and undesirable.

Everywhere the aim should be 'One Man, Many Votes'. Those who for this reason or that had no more than one would sleep happily at night, with their one vote under the pillow, proud of their place in the Constitution. Some would modestly desire no more: those who did would have to do what was necessary. Even in a 'true democracy' a man must take positive action to acquire a baby.

Members' Pay

REGINA *v.* WILPOT, M.P.

*(Before the Lord Chief Justice and the Judges
of the High Court sitting* in banc.)

THE Lord Chief Justice today gave judgment in this important
case concerning the recent increase in the remuneration of
Members of Parliament. He said:

This is in the nature of a test case which the Court has
considered at the request of the Speaker of the House of
Commons. The defendant, Mr Henry Wilpot, was elected to
the House of Commons by the delighted citizens of Burbleton
(West) in 1952. At that time the annual sum received by Members of Parliament – I use that cautious expression for reasons
which will appear later – was £1,000 a year. In the present
year there have been two or three debates concerning the
inadequacy of this sum and the propriety of an increase. It
was touching, one witness told the Court, to see what brotherly
love and forbearance was shown in these discussions by
Members of all parties, who in other subjects are accustomed
to address each other as if they were snakes or tigers. It was in
the end resolved by a large majority that an increase to £1,500
per annum was desirable and fitting. This decision was accepted
and executed by Her Majesty's Government and is now in
force. It was proved before us that the defendant has received,
and accepted, the first instalment of what the common people
would call his 'rise'.

With the ethics of these affairs this Court has nothing to do.
Indeed, it would ill become Her Majesty's Judges, who have
recently received a belated improvement in their own position,
to criticize the Members of Parliament, who also find themselves hardly pressed by the heavy expenditure of the State
and the cruel taxes for which they are responsible. Our task is
only to interpret the law.

Now, in 1707, in the reign of Queen Anne, was passed the Succession to the Crown Act. Section 25 provides that if any Member of Parliament

shall accept of any office of profit from the Crown, during such time as he shall continue a member, his election shall be and is hereby declared to be void and a new writ shall issue for a new election, as if such person so accepting, was naturally dead; provided nevertheless that such person shall be capable of being again elected.

The purpose of this arrangement, I think, is clear. For one thing, there may be some suspicion of nepotism or corruption, some question of unfitness in the appointment, which the sovereign people at a popular election may examine and condemn. For another – and this perhaps is more important – there has been a drastic change in the relations between the Member and his constituents. They chose a man who could serve them faithfully – and in those days serve for nothing – who would devote to their interests all his time and talents. Now, they find, he has sold his talents, and much of his time, to the Ministers. For all his fine professions at the election, the hope of profit, the greed for power, was hidden in his heart. He may, for all they know, have sacrificed his principles to secure his post. He may have put it out of his power to pursue with vigour the policies, the promises, for which they gave him their votes. Accordingly, they are given this opportunity to call him to account, to elect him again, if they are satisfied, and reject him if they are not.

In this case it is argued that these wholesome precautions ought to apply, and legally do apply, to Mr Wilpot. Again, there has been a drastic change in his relations with the people of Burbleton (West). They elected one man, and now they have another. Any ordinary man whose annual remuneration is suddenly advanced by a half – and there are not many – at once moves into another world. The defendant, in the box, admitted that at the election he said nothing about the inadequacy of the Parliamentary 'pay', nothing of any intention to press for an increase. On the contrary, according to the evidence, he asked with passionate eagerness to be sent to Parliament, though well aware of the terms and conditions of that employment. He also promised in many ways to secure an improvement in the lot of the poor: but these undertakings, through no fault of his own, perhaps, have not all been fulfilled. Further, the electors are now entitled to suspect that the man they chose for selfless service and philanthropic purpose had all the time in his heart the desire for profit and the intention to pursue it. In these circumstances it is not at all surprising if the electors wish him to vacate his seat and offer himself for election again. The question is, is that the law?

The Attorney-General, who appeared for the defendant, developed some arguments which may appeal to his Parliamentary colleagues, but will not, I fear, enhance his reputation at the Bar.

Sir Anthony Slatt, Q.C.: Milord, with great respect . . .

The Lord Chief Justice: Quiet, Sir Anthony.

He contended that the £1,500 was not 'profit and gains' but an 'allowance' towards the expenses of a legislator. If that were so the whole sum would be free of income tax. But, in fact, where a Member has other sources of income the Parliamentary 'pay' is lumped with them for purposes of income tax and surtax and, in fact, in many cases he enjoys the use of very little of it. The Court does not, as a rule, concern itself with the speeches of Members of Parliament: but here we take judicial notice of the fact that in a recent speech the Chancellor of the Exchequer referred more than once to the Member's 'salary'. So that cock must withdraw from the arena.

Then Sir Anthony said that membership of the House of Commons could not be described as an 'office'. In my opinion it can, for, according to the *Oxford English Dictionary*, an office means: 'A position or place to which certain duties are attached, especially one of a more or less public character; a position of trust, authority, or service under constituted authority; a place in the administration of government, the public service, etc.'

The Attorney-General argued then that if the defendant held an 'office of profit' he could not be said to hold it from the Crown. He is not in the employ of Ministers; indeed he belongs to the Opposition: and the money was voted by the House of Commons, in the name of the people. Yes, but it was the Crown, that is, the Ministers, who made the proposal. The Members may carry resolutions till they are tired: but without the deliberate initiative of the Crown these payments could never have been authorized or made. Technically, therefore, there is an opening for some of the very suspicions which prompted Section 25 of the Act of Queen Anne. Mr Wilpot and his friends may not be employed by the Crown, but they are beholden to the Crown. For all the elector knows there may have been some improper agreement or menace. The defendant and his friends may have undertaken not to oppose some Government measure, if this increase of salary were moved by the Ministers – they may have threatened to obstruct the Government business if it were withheld.

There is no evidence of any such thing: but that matters not at all. In most cases, in this honourable land, it will be found upon examination that such precautions were unnecessary: but that is not to say that they ought not to be scrupulously observed. Whatever ingenious play may be made with words and precedents, Mr Attorney, I find that in essence, in the conditions of the time, the facts are of the same character as our wise ancestors had in mind in 1707. The consequences must be the same. Mr Wilpot, and any other Member who has accepted the increase of salary, whether he voted for it or not, have vacated their seats, and new writs must issue for new elections. We are told that this may cause something like a General Election: but that does not concern the Court. The Members should have thought of that before.

All the Judges concurred.

31 May 1954

The Laws of Sunday

THERE was a startling turn to the Sunday Entertainment case at Bow Street this morning. In the dock was Mr R. Mortimer, charged with an offence against the Sunday Observance Act, 1781, which forbids the opening of any house, room, or place for any public entertainment 'to which persons are admitted by payment'. According to an information laid by the Sunday Society, Mr Mortimer was the promoter of a charity football match in aid of the Lawyers' Widows and Orphans Fund, in which twenty-two leading figures from stage and screen took part.

Mr Luke Goody, Secretary of the Sunday Society, gave evidence for the prosecution. The Chief Metropolitan Magistrate, Sir Richard Strong, said:

You, or your Society, originated this prosecution. But how do you know that the offence took place? Were you there?

Mr Goody : No, sir. On the Lord's Day I never leave my home. I read no newspapers. I allow the eating of no cooked food. I do not even answer the telephone, for this means labour on the Lord's Day.

Sir Richard : But if the unfortunate operator has to ring you three or four times, in vain, you have caused a lot more labour on the Lord's Day? (The witness did not reply.) Very well. At first hand you can tell me nothing about the offence. Is there anyone here who can tell us more?

Witness : Yes, sir, several of my workers were present.

Sir Richard : Let them be called.

Mr Wagwash, of the Sunday Society, testified that the match took place as alleged.

Sir Humphrey Baise (for the defence, in cross-examination) : Can you swear that any payment was made by the spectators?

Witness : Yes.

Sir Humphrey : How do you know?

Witness: I entered through a turnstile and paid five shillings for admission.

Sir Humphrey: When was the entertainment concluded?

Witness: At four o'clock.

Sir Humphrey: How do you know?

Witness: I was there.

Sir Humphrey: So you were present from first to last? Watching a football match? Do you think that is a proper way to spend the afternoon on the Lord's Day?

Witness: I was doing the Lord's work.

Sir Humphrey: The Court may have other opinions. This prosecution has been lodged by your Society under the Sunday Observance Act, 1781?

Witness: Yes, sir.

Sir Humphrey: Are you familiar with the Act of 1677?

Witness: I have read it. It is rarely used. You have to get the consent in writing of the chief of police, two justices of the peace, or a stipendiary.

Sir Humphrey: A pity. Let me read what it says: 'No tradesmen, artificers, workmen, labourers, or other persons whatsoever' – *or other persons whatsoever*, Mr Wagwash – 'shall do or exercise any worldly labour, business, or work of their ordinary callings upon the Lord's Day, or any part thereof (works of necessity or charity only excepted).' You are aware, Mr Wagwash, that the defendant, and those who assisted him, were engaged in an act of charity?

Witness: So they say. But the stars don't give these exhibitions for charity. They do it to get themselves publicity, and in that way they are really working.

Sir Humphrey: So your Secretary said in one of the newspapers. Not a very charitable judgment: but I am glad to have had it repeated in open court. Now, Mr Wagwash, you have been described by your Secretary as a 'worker' for the Society. Is that correct?

Witness: Yes, sir.

Sir Humphrey: Are you a paid worker?

Witness: Yes.

Sir Humphrey: You get an annual salary?

Witness : Yes.

Sir Humphrey : How much?

Witness : That's my business.

Sir Humphrey : Very well. Have you any other business?

Witness : Sir?

Sir Humphrey : Any other regular employment?

Witness : No.

Sir Humphrey : Now, Mr Wagwash, how would you describe your work?

Witness : Well, sir, we are always on the watch . . .

Sir Humphrey : For forthcoming breaches of the law?

Witness : Yes, sir. We study the newspapers. We follow up reports from local sympathizers. We write warning letters to the promoters, and so on.

Sir Humphrey : I see. And if these are not successful you attend the scene of the offence on Sunday, make notes, collect evidence, and so on?

Witness : Yes, sir.

Sir Humphrey : What made you act as you did last Sunday?

Witness : Instructions from Mr Goody, sir.

Sir Humphrey : Just so. Now Mr Wagwash, would it be fair to say that on the Sunday in question you were 'doing or exercising worldly labour'?

Witness : No, sir, it was labour for the Lord.

Sir Humphrey : But you were paid for it?

Witness : Clergymen are paid.

Sir Humphrey : But you are not a clergyman. I do not doubt your sincerity, Mr Wagwash. But you have chosen to earn money by this business of watching, protesting and, on the Lord's Day, spying.

Witness (hotly) : It's *not* spying.

Sir Humphrey : Very well – collecting evidence. Would you agree that the earning of money – except perhaps by clergymen – was a 'worldly' occupation?

Witness : Not in this case. It depends on the motive.

Sir Humphrey : Oh, does it? Then why are you so hot against the defendant, whose motive was charity?

Witness : That's different.

Sir Humphrey : Very well. You still don't agree that you were 'doing worldly labour' on Sunday last?

Witness : No.

Sir Humphrey : But at least, you will agree that, in the words of the Act of 1677, you were doing 'work of your ordinary calling' on the Lord's Day?

Witness : No.

Sir Humphrey : Perhaps you don't understand the word 'calling'. In the dictionary I have here it is described as 'trade, profession or vocation'. Did you not tell the Court just now that you have no other 'trade, profession, or vocation'?

Witness : That is so.

Sir Humphrey : Very well. Then this must be your 'ordinary calling'. But perhaps you rely on one of the exceptions. You would not suggest, I think, that your Sunday spying was a work of charity. Would you say that it was 'a work of necessity'?

Witness : Yes, sir. The law must be enforced.

The Chief Magistrate : At last I agree. Sir Humphrey, we need not trouble you more. Your able questioning has made it clear to my mind that the evidence supporting the prosecution was obtained by unlawful means, and it is to that extent severely tainted. The late and celebrated Lord Darling said once that the right way to be rid of a bad law was not to ignore but to enforce it. As a salaried magistrate I am qualified to authorize a prosecution under the Act of 1677, and I shall do so now. Not the unfortunate Mr Wagwash only. I find repelling the picture of the first witness, Mr Goody, sitting piously in his home on the Lord's Day, doing nothing, but sending his minions forth, to risk their souls, if no more, by this unpleasant, and, I believe, illegal espionage. He is at least an accessory before the act, and should appear with Wagwash and the other 'workers' before this Court this afternoon. As for the defendant Mortimer, I am bound to find him technically guilty, but he is unconditionally discharged.

Later today Goody, Wagwash and three others were found guilty of offences under the Act of 1677 and were fined 5s. each. The Society was ordered to pay the costs in all the prosecutions.

Interviewed, Mr Goody said 'It is a cruel dilemma. We must produce evidence. But if it is illegal to collect it, what are we to do?' 'Don't pay them,' a reporter suggested. But it is not certain that this precaution would be enough.

11 May 1960

Note: See also 'Sunday On the Air', *Codd's Last Case*, page 84, and Hansard, 1 April 1941 (Vol. 370, col. 959), when a Government motion to allow Sunday theatres in war-time was defeated by eight votes. Petty Officer Alan Herbert (Oxford University) said:

Let us look at what happened last Sunday. According to the *Radio Times*, there were no fewer than seven theatrical entertainments put forward by the B.B.C. last Sunday.

The entertainments, which were performed by professional actors, would be unlawful in the theatre outside. At 4.30 in the Home Service programme, at the time when in Victorian days the children were massing about their mothers' knees, there was a performance, with elaborate music and dialogue, of the degrading stage play called *Peter Pan*. It lasted one and a quarter hours. At 9.25 there was a play by the alien writer Euripides. The position was far more serious on the Forces programme, where there were at least five such performances. At 12.30 there was 'Services Variety', at 1.15 'Music Hall', and at 2.15 'Sunday Matinée', and at 6.30 something called 'Hi-Gang'. All these performances were given by well-known actors and actresses. At 8 o'clock an entertainment with the horrible name of 'Happidrome' was given. . .

Meanwhile, as my Hon. Friend has already pointed out, on Sunday in Fleet Street and in every other big town there were hundreds of thousands of men preparing Monday's *The Times* and *Express* and all the papers which my Hon. Friend reads in bed on a Monday without a protest or a qualm. Let me put it in another way. Take it from the point of view of a well-known actor, like John Gielgud. On Sunday, if the B.B.C. like, he can act *Hamlet* or *Henry V* all day long. He can appear on the films as Hamlet or Henry V. He can give a long lecture on *Hamlet* or *Henry V*. He can appear – this is remarkable – at a concert or cinema and act passages from *Henry V* so long as he does not make up, put on costume, and do the job properly. In other words, I think we are trying to keep the horse in the stable long after it is far away.

Codd's Last Case

REX *v*. RUNGLE

AT the Old Bailey today, after counsel's closing speeches in the
Burbleton Burglar case, the aged Mr Justice Codd summed up
to the jury. He said:

Gentlemen of the jury, this is a trial for murder – or maybe
manslaughter. A man's life hangs – pardon – depends upon
your decision: and you will, I know, approach your task with
due solemnity. So do I. But this is the last case that I shall ever
try. Once I'm back in the old flannel bags in the garden that
old Chief will never coax me into a Court again, whatever
epidemics may decimate the Bench. You, gentlemen, have spent
two or three days in a court of law, and already you are longing
to get back to civilization. I have been here for fifty years.
Imagine it! Fifty years of quarrelling and crime, quibbles and
costs, adulteries, assaults, burglaries and motor accidents.
'Running-down cases' we call them. Remember the story
about old Hewart, when he was Lord Chief Justice? Someone
asked him how he enjoyed his life on the Bench. 'It's all right,'
he said, 'when any legal business crops up. But I seem to spend
most of my time adjudicating on disputes between insurance
companies arising out of collisions between two stationary
motor-cars, each on the right side of the road, and blowing its
horn.' Ha! Yes, I thought you'd like that. Don't look so
shocked, Sir Roger. Mind you, gentlemen, I'm not complain-
ing. We like the life, of course: and we live a long time, I
can't think why. But fifty years, you may decide, is just
about enough. You may think, having heard all the evidence –
pardon me, I was forgetting – you want to hear about this
case.

Well, there is the prisoner, George Rungle. He's killed a
burglar, there's no doubt about that. But he looks a good chap,
you must agree. I believe he is a good chap: and I may as well
tell you at once that I'm on his side . . .

F

Sir Roger Wheedle (for the Crown): Milord! The jury can hardly . . .

The Judge: Of course, Sir Roger doesn't like that. I didn't expect he would. By the way, gentlemen, that's another big thing about my future. I shan't have to listen to any more speeches by my dear old colleague, Sir Roger Wheedle. You've heard one or two. I don't say they're not *good* speeches – they are: but you know what I mean. Going up now, aren't you, Sir Roger? Treasury briefs and all! The next thing, you'll be Solicitor-General. Which are you going to be, Conservative or Labour? Difficult to say just now, I suppose. Anyhow, you'll go far. You'll never sink to the Bench, like me. £5,000 a year, less two. Well, about this case. As I have said, there's no doubt that Mr Rungle killed this burglar.

Sir Ronald Rutt (for the defence): Milord, with great respect, that *is* one of the points on which . . .

The Judge: Now, what's the matter with you, Sir Ronald? By the way, how's your father? Dear old Ethelred! The battles we used to have! And how your dear father used to bristle! 'Bristle'! Yes, that's the word. And now he's up in the Court of Appeal. 'Lord Justice Rutt.' Soon be a Lord of Appeal, I shouldn't wonder. 'Baron Rutt.' I shall laugh, rather. Old Wool's there already. Can't be a day less than 103. But there he is; blowing off like a juvenile grampus. You've done well, too, young Ronald. I can see you President of the Board of Trade. And I'm still a miserable puisne in the King's Bench Division. Tomorrow I'll be plain Sir Humphrey Codd again. Never mind. About this case:

The prisoner killed the burglar. And what a good thing! If I have a chance, I'll kill a burglar too. What's more, it ought to be a capital offence. I never know why they make so much fuss about blackmail. After all, there couldn't be any blackmail if there wasn't something black to go upon. But these little squits of burglars – they creep into strange houses, poor houses too, frighten innocent old women and steal their wedding-rings. That's what this beast-boy had been doing for months! House after house. The police have got any number of . . .

Sir Roger Wheedle : With the greatest respect, milord . . .

The Judge : I know exactly what you're going to say, Sir Roger. So don't bother. That's what I think about burglars. You may say what you like about 'our barbarous ancestors', but in this department they knew a thing or two. In the eighteenth century – time of the *Beggar's Opera* – they were pretty harsh about stealing. They had to be. No police – no street-lamps – nothing. But they distinguished. If you stole property valued at five shillings you were hanged. If you stole from the person to the value of 1s., or from a dwelling-house to the value of 40s., you were hanged. But the juries were merciful, and scaled things down, if they liked your face. One Catherine Delavan, I remember, stole nine guineas and 11s.: but the jury found her guilty to the value of 4s. 10d. only. You see the point, Sir Roger? She was transported, not hanged.

Sir Roger Wheedle : The point is taken, milord.

The Judge : But there were two cases where no jury could save your neck. If you put people 'in Fear on the Highway', or if you burgled – that is, broke into a house *by night* – values didn't matter, and you were hanged, however little you stole. The same principle, no doubt – 'putting people in *fear*' – whether it was the highway or the house. When the deceased beast-boy had been at it for a month or two not a woman in the neighbourhood could sleep peacefully in her bed. At the smallest sound, the creak of a stair, the bang of a shutter, everyone in the house sat up sweating with alarm. That's why they hanged them in the eighteenth century, and that's why we ought to hang them now. The prisoner, of course, popped ahead and killed the burglar himself: and I must say that I'm delighted.

Sir Ronald Rutt : Milord . . .

Sir Roger Wheedle : Milord, with great respect, the laws of the eighteenth century are hardly on all fours with . . .

The Judge : All right, Sir Roger, let's come to the nineteenth century. Are you familiar with *Purcell's Case*?

Sir Roger Wheedle : No, milord.

The Judge : Well, Mr Purcell was a septuagenarian, of County Cork. And in 1811 he was knighted – *knighted*, Sir

Roger – for killing four burglars with a carving-knife. Pretty good, eh?

Sir Roger Wheedle: That, no doubt, was in self-defence, milord. In the present case, the deceased was offering no violence and in fact was leaving the premises.

The Judge: But he had offered violence, he had committed a violent felony, and he was escaping. You see what it is, members of the jury? They're trying to whittle down our ancient rights. It's all part of this namby-pamby stuff about crime. I expect Sir Roger Wheedle's heart is bleeding for the deceased, the little pest. What was the burglar's name, Sir Roger?

Sir Roger: Moss, milord. And may I add, milord, that I am only trying to seek the truth and to do my duty according to the law.

The Judge: Of course, Sir Roger, of course! Don't excite yourself. But you know Moss's record as well as I do. Left a good home and joined a gang. Began coshing at the age of twelve. Brought up in luxury at remand schools and approved schools and Lord knows what. Had every chance. Never done a day's work. Doesn't mind prison because it's all so cosy now. Keeps a whole neighbourhood in terror for weeks. And when he catches it at last we're told an unkind charwoman shut him in a cupboard when he was a child, and he's never been the same since. He's a pathological case or a psychological misfit.[1] Ha! Stuff and nonsense! Suffers from 'frustration'. Frustration, indeed! I wonder how they'd like to be a judge in these days, drawing the same pay for the last hundred years and more!

Sir Roger: Milord, with great respect, the character of the deceased is not strictly . . .

The Judge: I know. I know. I'm wandering, Sir Roger. But you provoked me. What I mean is that no one seems to bother about the psychology of the poor old men and women who lie shivering in their beds when a beast-boy's about. And when he gets his deserts . . .

1. See *Rex* v. *Lout* (1951), where a youth was charged with robbery with violence and other offences. His father said: 'At the age of fourteen he fell out of a tree. Since then he's been a different boy.'

Sir Roger : Milord!

The Judge : Don't interrupt, Sir Roger. We must get on. Now, jurymen all, recall what happened. Mr Rungle, having no firearms, kept an ordinary garden-fork by his bed, as we all ought to do. That, or a hat-pin. At two o'clock in the morning he hears noises below; he takes his garden-fork, slips downstairs, and finds Moss, in a mask, filling a bag with the Rungle goods and belongings. Moss held a pistol at him (it wasn't loaded, but Rungle was not to know that), and in the childish language of his kind, said: 'Stick 'em up. This is a stick-up.' Rungle bravely, and rather wittily, replied, raising his garden-fork: 'Oh, is it? And this is a stick-*in*! Ha!'

When the bold burglar saw the garden-fork, he uttered a yell of terror, turned and made for the window. Mr Rungle cried, 'Stop!' meaning to arrest him; but Moss did not stop. As he was passing through the window the prisoner threw the garden-fork after him, harpoon-fashion: it pierced the burglar's heart and he died.

Now, the Crown, rather mildly, it is true, suggest to you that this was Murder. The defence say that it was Justifiable Homicide.

Sir Roger, I know, does not think that I know any law, though in fifty years one does pick up some scraps of information. So I have been looking up the authorities, and, in these soft days, it does appear that there is some doubt. In one tremendous tome (under *Burglary*) I read:

The question whether and how far it is justifiable to kill a burglar is by no means clear. If violence on the part of the burglar is reasonably apprehended, it is not murder to shoot him dead with intent to kill him, but whether it is justifiable to kill merely in defence of property is doubtful.

But in another page of the same tome I find two of the categories of Justifiable Homicide set out as follows:

(*d*) Where an officer or his assistant, in the due execution of his office, arrests or attempts to arrest a person for *felony*, or a dangerous wound given, and he having notice thereof flies and is killed by such officer or assistant in pursuit.

(e) Where upon such offence as last described *a private person* in whose sight it has been committed arrests or endeavours to arrest the offender, and kills him in resistance or flight, in similar circumstances.

Note, gentlemen, that burglary is a felony, and a violent felony.

I turned then to Mr Kenny's admirable *Outlines of Criminal Law*.[1] Here again I wandered, as one wanders in a wood, now in sunlight, now in the shade. First I was told, with some discouragement, that:

When the wrongdoer is not going so far as to assault a human being, but is only *interfering unlawfully with property*, whether real or personal, the possessor of that property (though he is permitted by the law to use a moderate degree of force in defence of his possessions) will usually not be justified in carrying this force to the point of killing the trespasser. . . .

But then I passed into the light:

Such a justification will not arise unless the trespasser's interference or resistance amounts to a felony, and moreover to a felony of some kind that is violent, such for example, as robbery, arson or *burglary*.

One more step and I was in the shade again:

Even these extremely violent felonies should not be resisted by extreme violence unless it is actually necessary; thus, firearms should not be used unless there seems to be no other mode ('Mode!' I like 'mode', don't you?) available for defeating the intruder *and securing his arrest*.

Sir Roger Wheedle: Your lordship, no doubt, remembers the case of *Rex* v. *Cooper*?

The Judge: You mean that case in 1641? At the Surrey Assizes?

Sir Roger: Yes, milord.

The Judge: Of course. But I don't see that it helps you much. That was another window case. Cooper struck a burglar in the eye with a spit. And was acquitted.

1. Cambridge University Press.

Sir Roger : Yes, milord. But, milord, I should be prepared to distinguish.

The Judge : You can't distinguish any more. Well, gentlemen, there you are. The Crown's case, I gather – and, by the way, I'm not sure that they believe in it very strongly, but they think, in these days, they have to be as soft as they can – where was I ? Oh, yes, the Crown's case is that Rungle was not being attacked, and was in no danger himself; that the deceased beast-boy was merely interfering, or had merely interfered, with property (and property, of course, is very unpopular nowadays), therefore the prisoner was entitled only to use *reasonable* force: to stick a man through the heart with a garden-fork was more than reasonable in the circumstances, and therefore the killing was murder. Is that a fair statement of your case, Sir Roger?

Sir Roger : Yes, milord. I might add, of course . . .

The Judge : But you mayn't. Now, gentlemen of the jury, I must not, of course, attempt to influence you unduly (what an idea!). But let me tell you the story as I see it in the light of the law, as I understand it.

The deceased Moss committed a burglary. At Common Law this crime is committed when a dwelling-house or a church is broken into and entered at night with the intention of committing some felony therein. Section 51 of the Larceny Act, 1861, extended the definition.

Whosoever shall enter the dwelling-house of another with intent to commit any felony therein, or being in the said dwelling-house shall commit any felony therein, and shall in either case break out of the said dwelling-house in the night, shall be deemed guilty of burglary.

Now, burglary, I say again, is a felony and a 'violent' felony. It is a continuing offence. A man is a burglar from the time he breaks in till the time he breaks out. He does not cease to be a burglar if, having robbed the house, he sits down in an armchair and peaceably recites the poems of Keats. In this case he made a feeble threat of violence to the householder: but I am willing to forget that, if it pleases Sir Roger; for it is not necessary to my argument. The big point is that the house-holder finds the felon at work; that not only his instinct, and his interest, but his public duty instruct and oblige him to arrest the felon, if he can, and to hand him over to justice. There have been numerous burglaries in the neighbourhood which have gone unpunished (few indeed are the arrested burglars anywhere, and sadly few the stolen goods recovered). A householder is in the position of an unofficial police officer: if he lets the felon go he will be letting loose a menace to who knows how many other defenceless homes. Accordingly he orders the felon to 'Stop!' But the felon ('he having notice thereof') makes off. What is the householder to do? He can only use the nearest weapon to his hand. If Mr Rungle had had a fire-arm he would have been well entitled to shoot the burglar in the leg, at least. As it was, he had only a garden-fork. He did not, I am sure, intend to kill the burglar. The one thought, the proper thought, in his mind, was 'I must stop him' (and let us not forget that the word 'arrest' means 'stop'). It is regrettable perhaps (though not, I think, very much) that his only weapon had the result it did: but for that there is nobody to blame but the burglar. As the harsh but wholesome saying goes, 'He should have thought of that before' – before, that is, he entered upon a crime which has rightly earned especial detestation from the State.

'Now, gentlemen, I have done. I should not like my last judicial utterance to be quoted as something exceptional, relevant only to the circumstances of a special case. No, Sir Roger, since there appears to be some doubt in this important corner of life and law, I declare the law to be as follows:

'It is the right and duty of any householder, or any other honest citizen, who finds an undoubted burglar in a dwelling-house, to arrest him. He may, and should, order the burglar to stay quietly on the premises till any necessary arrangements have been made. If the burglar disobeys this order and attempts to make off, the honest citizen may use any force he considers necessary and any weapon that is at hand to stop him: and if the result is death it is justifiable homicide; not murder, or even manslaughter.'

But, of course, gentlemen, you are the jury: and you are well entitled to say that I am talking nonsense. Pray consider your verdict.

The Foreman stood up and called for three cheers for his lordship. Then, without leaving the box, they found the prisoner Not Guilty.

The Judge : Discharge the prisoner. Good-bye, Mr Rungle. Kill all the burglars you can. But don't forget to say 'Stop!'

Sir Roger Wheedle : Milord, if you can stand one more speech from me, I should like, on behalf of the Bar, to wish you a long and happy retirement.

Sir Ronald Rutt : I too, milord.

The Judge : Well that's very handsome of you both. I must say I've enjoyed my last case considerably. If you aren't careful, I shall come back after all.

7 September 1951

Note: Unhappily, in a later case, the Lord Chief Justice overruled and rejected Codd J.'s pronouncement: 'It is not in accordance with the tender spirit or the enlightened thinking of the time. Property is not the sacred cause that it was; for many it is almost a crime. . . . It must be recognized that every burglar has a mother, and, through the ill-treatment of society, is likely to be a sufferer from psychological lesions. If it were once to get about that householders were able and willing to pursue the successful robber with fire-arms, the burglar, in self-defence, would be compelled to carry a pistol, a great inconvenience to his profession, and a danger to others.' (See *Regina* v. *Hockey – Bardot, M.P.*, page 32.)

Felony and Misdemeanour

REX *v*. SMITH

THIS was an appeal to the High Court upon a case stated by a Metropolitan magistrate.

The Lord Chief Justice: This is one of the cases in which His Majesty's judges, through no fault of their own, are unable to do justice and can but gloomily enforce the law and respectfully condemn the Legislature. The appellant, Mr Smith, was passing peacefully along a London street when he observed a miscreant ripping the tyres of an unattended and stationary motor-car. A man of more than usual courage and determination, Mr Smith seized the man and succeeded in detaining him by force until a police-constable arrived. The malefactor was duly prosecuted and punished for his offence; but, having, it appears, some knowledge of the law, he issued a counter-summons against Mr Smith for assault, upon which Mr Smith was convicted. Against this conviction Mr Smith has appealed.

I am sorry to have to say that the magistrate was right and that Mr Smith was properly convicted. Mr Smith may well be surprised, for the citizen is frequently informed that it is the duty of all able-bodied persons to assist the officers of the law to the utmost of their powers in the prevention of crime and, in certain circumstances, the apprehension of the criminal. Unfortunately the important words in the sentence last spoken are the words, 'in certain circumstances', and they are the snare into which the gallant Mr Smith has fallen.

Mr Smith's conviction rests upon the ancient but now, in substance, meaningless distinction between felony and misdemeanour, which ought to be abolished.

All indictable offences are either felonies or misdemeanours. A felony, at Common Law, was a crime so strongly deprecated by the State that, apart from any other punishment, it involved the forfeiture of the offender's property. Lesser crimes were

known as 'Transgressions' or 'Trespasses', and later 'Misdemeanours', and these did not inevitably carry forfeiture.
Statutes from time to time added new crimes to both categories. Originally all felonies (except petty larceny) were
punished with death, but not misdemeanours. Forfeiture for
felony, however, was abolished in 1870, and the death penalty
is now practically restricted to the felony of murder (though I
must warn Mr Haddock, if he is in Court, that he may still be
hanged for setting fire to a Royal Dockyard or to any ship in the
Port of London). Thus the origins of the distinction have disappeared, and there appears to be no logical ground for its
retention. Yet it survives.

Felonies, to particularize, include murder, suicide, manslaughter, burglary, housebreaking, embezzlement, larceny,
and bigamy; while some of the better-known *misdemeanours*
are perjury, conspiracy, fraud, libel, false pretences, riot, and
assault.

It cannot even be said that all felonies are more repellent
crimes than all misdemeanours; for it is a felony to steal a
penny, but only a misdemeanour to defraud a man of a million
pounds. Most of us would think that perjury, conspiracy, and
criminal libel were offences at least as dangerous and detestable
as a mild burglary or inadvertent act of bigamy. But the former
are misdemeanours only and the latter felonies. Perjury, as
the admirable Mr Kenny has pointed out,[1] may cause the death
of an innocent person, yet is only a misdemeanour; while it
is a felony to keep a horse-slaughterer's yard without a licence.
Embezzlement is a felony but fraud a misdemeanour. To carry
off a young woman is sometimes one and sometimes the other.

If it were only an historical curiosity, like the Woolsack,
which did not impede the flow of justice, I should not have
much to say against this quaint old classification of offences.
Unfortunately some practical consequences of importance do
still proceed from it.

For example, the convicted felon loses any office or pension;
he cannot vote for nor sit in Parliament, nor hold military or civil
or ecclesiastical office until he has been pardoned or has worked

1. *Outlines of Criminal Law.*

out his sentence. 'These disqualifications' (I am again quoting the good Mr Kenny) 'are not entailed by any misdemeanour.' So that if a Bishop, Colonel or Member of Parliament commits a burglary he will be deprived of his office; but if he is found guilty of perjury or fraud he may still, so far as the Common Law is concerned, continue to be a Bishop, Colonel, or Member of Parliament, as the case may be.

I now come to the strange but, to the appellant, vital distinction which in the present case must govern this reluctant Court. Since felonies were at one time the most heinous of offences, the immediate apprehension of the felon was of paramount importance to the State; and in an age when the officers of justice were less numerous and well-equipped than they are today, wide powers of arrest were granted not only to the constable but to the private citizen. Any person – constable or citizen – who sees a felony committed not only may but *must*, so far as his powers permit, arrest the felon at once; and he may use any violence that may be necessary to do so. Further, if the felony has already been committed the law permits the private citizen to arrest another whom he suspects upon reasonable grounds to be guilty.

But in the case of a misdemeanour the Common Law was more cautious. Not even an eye-witness of a misdemeanour might arrest the offender without first obtaining a warrant from a magistrate; and that is still the law, apart from certain exceptions introduced by statute – as, for example, where a private citizen finds another signalling to a smuggling vessel, committing an offence against the Coinage Offences Act, 1861, or, upon certain conditions, the Malicious Damage Act, 1861.

Now, to slash the tyres of a stationary motor-car is not a felony but a misdemeanour; nor is it covered by any of the statutory exceptions to the general rule, for private motor-cars were not imagined by the authors of the Malicious Damage Act, 1861.

At law, therefore, Mr Smith was not entitled to seize the body of the miscreant. His proper course was to stand at a reasonable distance and deliver a moral address upon the iniquity of malicious damage. He might, I think, have added a warning that if the miscreant was not careful he would tell his mother; but even this might have made Mr Smith liable to a summons for using abusive or threatening language.

I would add, for the general guidance of citizens like Mr Smith who go about seeking to protect the lives and property of their fellow-citizens, the following rule of conduct: 'Ignorance of the law excuses no man'; and, though there are vast areas of the law with which I am not familiar, the citizen is expected to know it all.

Mr Smith, then, and those like him, must study the textbooks upon criminal law until they have mastered the differences between felony and misdemeanour. If they are unable to commit them to memory they should carry upon their persons a list – or rather two lists, in parallel columns – of the various indictable offences, the felonies on one side and the misdemeanours on the other. On perceiving another citizen engaged in what appears to be a violent and unlawful act, they should not lay hands upon him until they have consulted their lists and assured themselves that the circumstances are such as to justify them in making an arrest. If after this precaution they are still in doubt as to the precise nature of the offence, or if they have mislaid their lists, the only proper course is to invite the assistance of the miscreant, who, *ex hypothesi*, should know better than any other citizen what class of offence he is committing.

A man who is found handling documents in an office after working-hours may be guilty of housebreaking, embezzlement, or larceny (which are felonies), or only of fraud or trespass (which are misdemeanours), or perhaps of forgery (which may be either one or the other); and before Mr Smith takes the risk of arresting him the man should be asked to make his position clear. In the present case Mr Smith should have said, 'Pardon me, sir, but in your opinion is your conduct felonious? *Prima facie*, I should say that it was covered by the Malicious Damage Act, 1861, but in the laws of England, as you know, there is many an unsuspected hiatus, and, unhappily, I have left my copy of the Statute Book at home. If you yourself are in any doubt, sir, the simplest course would be for you, first, to strike

me on the nose and then to threaten to do it again; for I am
entitled to arrest a person committing a breach of the peace in
my presence and while there is danger that the peace may continue to be broken.' If during this address the miscreant had
made off, Mr Smith would at least have put himself on the right
side of the law. As it was, he neglected these simple precautions and he has been properly convicted of assault.

The appeal is dismissed.

11 October 1933

Note: Progress bustles along. In his Election Address of 1935
your editor wrote: 'The antiquated distinctions between felony
and misdemeanour should be abolished.' In 1965, thirty years
later, a law reform committee came to the same conclusion. It
would be almost culpable euphoria to suppose that anything is
likely to happen.

'Cheap Literature'

REGINA *v.* DARK AND HADDOCK

AT Bow Street today the Chief Magistrate, Sir Raven Wren, gave a vigorous decision in the Privileged Libraries case. He said:

This was an information laid by the British Museum, the Bodleian Library, the University Library, Cambridge, the National Library of Scotland, the National Library of Wales, and the Library of Trinity College, Dublin, against Mr Alan Dark, a publisher, for an offence under Section 15 of the Copyright Act, 1911. One Haddock, an author, is charged with conspiracy, incitement, aiding and abetting, and all that kind of thing.

This, I suppose, is the most impudent prosecution that ever came before this Court. It is a shameless attempt to enforce through the criminal law what can only be described as a piece of statutory robbery against some of the best and poorest citizens, the authors and publishers of our land.

Section 15 of the Copyright Act, 1911, provided, astonishingly, as follows:

(1) The publisher of every book published in the United Kingdom shall within one month of the publication deliver, *at his own expense,* a copy of the book to the trustees of the British Museum, who shall give a written receipt for it.

(2) He shall also, if written demand is made within twelve months . . . deliver a copy of the book (to each of the five other prosecutors).

Subsection (6) provided penalties:

If a publisher fails to comply with this section he shall be liable on summary conviction to a fine not exceeding five pounds and the value of the book, and the fine shall be paid to the trustee or authority to whom the book ought to have been delivered.

Observe that it is a criminal offence for a publisher to fail to give his goods away for nothing; and for that offence the honest Mr Dark now stands in the dock.

All this is not, unfortunately, new: it goes back to an Act of 1775, and even further. Sir Thomas Bodley, it seems, obtained a grant from the Stationers' Company of every work printed in the country in 1610. According to a Royal Commission of 1878 the other obligations dated from the time of Charles II and an Act of 1662. The publishers affirmed, in 1911, that 'the exaction is the remnant of an enactment connected with the literary censorship established after the Reformation and intended to prevent the publication of heretical, blasphemous, immoral, or seditious books.' The Royal Commission of 1878, by the way, recommended that the provisions should be repealed except so far as they related to the British Museum. The 1911 Section did not become law without protest from authors and publishers, and there were long and strong debates in the House of Lords,[1] led by the great Lord Gorell.

The Copyright Act, 1956, repealed nearly all of the Act of 1911, but carefully preserved this Section, with one other. It seems to me that here is a shocking tale of gracious gestures abused and exploited. It was one thing, two or three centuries ago, when the libraries were young and struggling, for the Monarch or the Stationers' Hall to give them special privileges. It is quite another thing today, when these great libraries have the force and sometimes the funds of the State behind them, to impose by Act of Parliament compulsory charity on authors and publishers who stand alone, without subsidy or assistance from any quarter.

Nor is this, as we had thought, a small affair. More than 23,000 books were published last year in the United Kingdom; and most of these are in fact demanded and delivered. It may be right, the defendant Dark conceded, that the British Museum should have every book that appears and he delivers all his own books to the Museum himself. But he made much the same complaint that was made by Lord Gorell, who said that 'in course of time it has become the practice of the other libraries to apply for a copy of every book published, including

1. Hansard (Lords), Vol. X, cols 173 and 468.

a vast mass of printed matter which cannot possibly be of any use to them'. A single agent, it appears, serves the five libraries and with some exceptions demands everything – 'to be on the safe side'. Thus, taking 23s. as the average price of a modern book,[1] we conclude that the six prosecutors are receiving free about 140,000 volumes, or £160,000 worth of books, for which the publisher receives no profit and the author no royalty. Dark gave the Court some special examples of hardship. Suppose, he said, that out of the goodness of his heart he prints an expensive and almost certainly unprofitable volume of the folios of Shakespeare – fifty copies at fifteen guineas – it is no trifling injury to be required to give away six of those precious copies: and there are publications even more expensive than that. In no other country are so many free copies exacted.

Another publisher, with evident reluctance, told us about one of the prosecutors, Trinity College, Dublin. When Eire left the Commonwealth the publishers naturally inquired whether they were still bound to supply this alien college with their authors' books for nothing. Our Minister of Education, it seems, desired them to 'make no fuss', and to continue to bestow their books as a 'cultural gesture'. The publishers generously agreed: for Trinity College has strong links with England. By the Act of 1956, Parliament, in its wisdom, con-tinued, at the publishers' expense, the benefaction to Trinity College, Dublin.

Goaded, he admits, by one of his authors, the defendant Haddock, Dark has declined to deliver to the six prosecutors copies of one of Haddock's fascinating works, *Re-name the Stars*. Haddock, in evidence, said that as a patriot he was proud of the British Museum; that as an Oxford man he was devoted to the great Bodleian; that his father was a student at Trinity College, Dublin, that his middle name was Patrick, that he felt a firm affection for the Irish. He would be delighted, as an act of grace, to present his books, if they are needed, to these three libraries himself, as he does in fact to the House of Commons. But, he added, 'There comes a time when sentiment must stand aside for justice. This law is an important example of the

1. It is now (1966) said to be more like 30s.

attitude of the State and Parliament to the literary craft
and trade. Everything is rightly done for those who need
books; but there is not sufficient thought for those who produce
them. We have become a nation of book-borrowers, with a
vast and splendid library system; but authors and publishers
can only live by the sale of books. The 'free' Public Libraries
issue on loan, for nothing, 460,000,000 books a year – this
enormous figure has grown from a mere 76 million in 1924.
Parliament, in 1892, forbade the Public Libraries to make any
charge to the borrower: and that is still the law. A single book
(with one re-binding) may be issued to 200 citizens: but for
this one volume the author will receive a single royalty of
1s. 6d. to 2s. 6d., and the publisher a similar sum; while the
people have enjoyed £200 worth of reading without payment,
except through the rates. When the Copyright Act of 1911 was
before the House of Commons, one Member, Mr Booth, said
that "he had had communications from all over the country,
from working men, who properly consider it an attack on their
right and privilege to *cheap literature*".[1] That is very fine: but
authors and publishers conceive that they have a right and
privilege to earn their living and pay their bills. In small but
civilized Denmark the harsh lot of the authors has been
recognized and relieved through a Government grant by way of
'Library Royalties'. Here . . .'

At this point I had to check the witness for irrelevance. But
his roving testimony satisfied me at least that the action of the
two defendants was more in the nature of a political demon-
stration or protest than an assault upon the ancient prosecuting
libraries; and this has assisted me. I am bound, formally, to
find both men guilty. Dark, accordingly, will pay a fine of 1s. plus
15s. the value of the book, to each of the first five prosecutors.
(I except Trinity College, Dublin, on the grounds of public
policy, which must forbid the payment of a fine to a foreign
institution no longer in the Commonwealth.) But there will
be a stay of execution for ten years, which should give Parliament time to alter the law. I hope there will be no long delay;
for if every publisher takes it into his head to do as Mr Dark has

1. Hansard, Vol. XXVIII, col. 1903.

done we shall have 23,000 prosecutions on our hands, and the law may begin to look pretty silly.

The man Haddock is bound over to be of good behaviour, but not for very long. The entire costs of the prosecution will be paid by the prosecutors.

4 January 1961

Note: Mr Haddock, in a statement after the case, said:

This has been described as one of the oldest living controversies. The student will enjoy the three eloquent and informative debates in the House of Lords, 1911, notably a passage in Column 196, Volume X:

The Lord Archbishop of Canterbury: My Lords, I stand before your Lordships in an unwonted capacity – as a member of the Board of Trade. I do not know who the other members are, or whether they ever meet.

All the great names appeared. 'In 1836,' Lord Curzon, Chancellor of Oxford University, revealed, 'the curators of the Bodleian Library were offered five hundred pounds by the Government to surrender their privilege, but so much value did they attach to it that they declined the offer. . . .' The Scots, strangely enough, were not so shrewd. Under a Statute of Queen Anne (1709) Scotland had five libraries on the free list, but they agreed to be bought out.

No noble Lord paid the slightest attention to the Royal Commission of 1878, though it was mentioned. Lord Gorell, champion of the book-producers, merely, and mildly, asked that (except for the British Museum) there should be 'some control or some check upon the right to demand *every* book that is published' – as there was to be, and is, in the case of Wales.

Lord Cromer quoted an article written by the poet Southey in 1819:

The publishers were told that the public bodies would exercise their claims mildly and liberally, that they would take lists and only call for such books as they absolutely wanted, that their main object was to *establish* their right, but trust them, and it should be seen how they used the power. See, indeed, how they use it!

'In the course of time,' said Lord Cromer, ninety-two years later, 'it has become the practice . . . to apply for a copy of every book published, including a vast mass of printed matter which

cannot possibly be of any use to them' and much that is not
'really necessary or desirable for the libraries'. (Col. 178.)

He mentioned the expensive and limited editions; for example:

The *Bridgewater Gallery* ... the cost price of which was fifty guineas ...
The publishers are making a present of goods which they value at
two hundred and fifty guineas, and I think it is asking a good deal of
them.

He was very severe about:

The Story of Emma, Lady Hamilton, published at thirty guineas . . .
This work consists of a story of Lady Hamilton's youth and contains
reproductions in photogravure of a number of those celebrated pictures
of Romney representing this remarkable lady as Circe, Euphrosyne,
the Nun, St Cecilia, the Spinster, and several times as a Bacchante. I
can hardly conceive a work of a less academic character or one less
necessary for the tuition, instruction, and edification either of the
authorities at the Universities or of those students who flock for
instruction and study to the Bodleian Library. (Col. 181.)

But Lord Curzon vigorously replied:

The noble Earl . . . spoke of the Bodleian Library as if it were purely
an academic institution existing solely for the instruction of Dons and
undergraduates. He even put the case of the history of Lady Hamilton
and asked what was the good of giving a book of that sort to the
Bodleian Library. It would, he said, hardly appeal to the Dons – about
which I am not at all certain – and it ought not to appeal to the undergraduates, about which I am even less sure. But . . . the Bodleian is
more than an academic institution. It is . . . a great national institution,
one of the principal repositories of literature in this country. (Col. 184.)

He continued:

Is it wise, even admitting the special character of the British Museum,
that you should treat that as the only great national repository of
published books in this country? Supposing some great conflagration
were to occur and the British Museum were to be wrecked and its
contents destroyed, what a lamentable thing it would be if there were
no other institution to which to turn than that which you had unfortunately lost!

No one will quarrel with that. We simply ask why such
'national institutions' should be kept alive by the publishers,
and to a lesser degree the authors. Sir Henry Craik, a University
Member, said in the House of Commons, in 1911, on the pro-

posal to add Wales to the free list: 'My objection is not to the grant of books, but to the grant being made in the form of a tribute from a particular trade.'

Lord Curzon said: 'I do not think it is anything more than a slight burden.' But in 1911 perhaps 7,000 books were published. In 1962 the figure was 23,200 and the average price about 23s. As production and prices continue to increase so will the burden on the book-producers.

Lord Curzon said:

The question is whether it is a burden that they can legitimately be ordered to bear. I think it is for these reasons. In the first place, publishers as a body gain enormously by the privileges (?) conceded to them in the Copyright Act . . . and those privileges are really enhanced under this Bill. Publishers, on the whole, and authors with them, are placed in a better position. It is, therefore, not unreasonable to ask that they should make some return to the public for the privileges that they enjoy. (Col. 185.)

Lord Haldane too had said, moving the second reading:

It is complained that it is a burden on publishers to supply these books. So it is. But it must be remembered that publishers are getting protection under this Bill of a new kind. (Col. 46.)

Some of us remember the same reply being given in Whitehall during the passing of the Copyright Act of 1956. 'We are giving you something in this Bill. Why make a fuss about the free books?'

The publishers gave way, meekly muttering the last lines of Hymn A & M 224:

> O happy band of publishers,
> Look upward to the skies,
> Where such a light affliction
> Shall win so great a prize.

The argument is impudent, and does not impress. We are duly grateful to Parliament for the laws of copyright; but what we enjoy through them is not properly described as 'privileges'. They are protection against cheating and stealing such as the law provides for other forms of property. No such tribute, we believe, is demanded of scientific inventors who 'enjoy the privileges' of patent law. There have been special statutes concerned with 'poaching': but the grateful landlords were not, and are not, required to send thank-offerings of game, in per-petuity, to the Exchequer.

Lord Curzon, leaping like some nimble chamois from one effrontery to another, said:

> If I were a publisher I would rather be disposed to welcome the *gratuitous form of advertisement* for important books which I thus obtained. (Col. 185.)

This was the cry of the infant B.B.C., and is now the cry of the Public Libraries. 'Not much cash, old boy. But look at the publicity!' We wonder what the motor manufacturers would say if they were told: 'You will all be compelled by law to give six of your new models to the State. But cheer up! Just think of the advertisement.'

In 1961 Mr Nigel Fisher, M.P., took the matter up, in vain. One junior Minister made the surprising assertion that, 'We have not so far received any complaint from the publishers.'

On 11 July, in reply to a supplementary question in which Mr Fisher asked whether 'the cost to the authors and publishers is about £100,000 per annum', Mr Maudling, for the Board of Trade, said:

> I think that my Hon. Friend is possibly over-estimating the burden on the publishers. [Not in the least.] In 1952 the Copyright Committee said:
>
> 'In view of the long-standing nature of the privilege and obligation and what we feel to be the comparatively slight burden it creates for the publishing trade as a whole in relation to their turnover we do not recommend the discontinuance of the custom.'
>
> I think that, on the whole, I would agree with that.

We may observe that if the burden on the publishing trade is comparatively slight it would be unnoticeably infinitesimal as an item in the expenditure of the State. Whatever may be thought of the dimensions of the burden we are shocked by the fact that since the Royal Commission of 1878 no official body has admitted the iniquity of the principle. But if the principle is admitted where are these exactions to stop? We foresee a day when the 'red-brick' Universities (there are twenty of them already, and more imagined) will say, with some force: 'Why should the ancient places alone have these privileges? We babies need them even more. Why should we not get our books for nothing from the publishers? Are we not as deserving as Trinity College, Dublin?'

Would free books for twenty-six libraries (a mere £700,000) still be regarded as a 'comparatively slight burden'?

Authors are less affected directly, but everything that touches the publisher touches them; and they should, perhaps, protest more than they do. No individual author loses more than six royalties for each new book (or new edition): but the total loss of royalties must be between £15,000 and £16,000 a year, and, failing all else, it would be a pleasing gesture if the State made over such a sum to the Society of Authors.

(One Minister in 1961 made the astonishing statement that the present arrangements 'need not penalize authors at all' meaning that the publishers should add the cost of royalties to the cost of providing, packing and dispatching 140,000 free books. It has always been the custom to exclude from royal payments books given away, whether compulsorily to the privileged libraries, or voluntarily to newspapers for review and public purposes. No author expects, or would think of asking for a royalty upon them.)

Authors use the libraries themselves, and are grateful. They have too, like the publishers, a strong sense of service to the public. They think themselves fortunate that the purpose of their work and calling is to instruct or entertain, or please in other ways, their fellow-men. But, also, we favour fair-play and decent dealing. Too often, it seems to us, our gentle feelings are abused by the rulers, or taken too much for granted. This ancient business of the free books is a gross example. We should all support the publishers in resisting statutory robbery, and never let the grievance die.

The expression 'Copyright' Libraries, by the way, is a meaningless misnomer: the privileged libraries acquire nothing in the nature of copyright.

Good Old *Scire Facias*!

HADDOCK *v*. THE ARTS COUNCIL OF GREAT BRITAIN

(*Before a Divisional Court*)

MR JUSTICE LARK, giving judgment today, said:

This captivating bicker began with a polite writ of *Quaere transgressit* requiring the Arts Council of Great Britain to show cause why it has exceeded the instructions and conditions which govern its existence.

The Council was incorporated by Royal Charter on 9 August 1946:

for the purpose of developing greater knowledge, understanding and practice of *the fine arts exclusively*, and in particular to increase the accessibility of the fine arts to the public . . . to improve the standard of execution of the fine arts and to advise and cooperate with . . . Government Departments, Local Authorities and other bodies on any matters directly or indirectly concerned with those objects . . .

The sixteen Members of the Council are appointed by the Treasury, from which it receives an annual grant. Among other laudable activities it finances the performance of Grand Opera and Ballet at Covent Garden and Sadler's Wells; it supports the London Philharmonic, the Hallé and other symphony orchestras; the Old Vic and Nottingham Theatre Trusts, the English Stage Company, the Birmingham Repertory, and other repertory theatres all over the country. The public funds, we were told, between 1945 and 1956 contributed £1,778,000 towards the losses sustained by the Covent Garden Opera House, so that the questions raised in the case are of more than academic interest.

A notable omission from the objects of the Council's aid is 'literature' – and this is one of the plaintiff's grievances. But in recent years a slightly helping hand has been held out to Poetry. In 1961–2 the total expenditure was £1,598,201. Of this sum £1,216,937, or 76 per cent, went to Music: £256,007 (or 16 per cent) to Drama, and only £79,000, (or 4·9 per cent) to Art. Poetry got £4,581 (or 0·3 per cent): the small remainder went to Festivals and Art Clubs.[1]

Thus 92 per cent of the money went to Music and Drama, and less than 5 per cent to Art. The State patronage of Music, by the way, was not quite so generous as it sounds: for what it bestowed with one hand it took away with the other by an uncivilized tax on musical instruments. As Sir Malcolm Sargent stands with baton poised at the opening of the 'Pathetic' Symphony he may well feel grateful to the Treasury which is helping to keep his mighty orchestra in being: but he will reflect with melancholy that every instrument about him (except the piano) has paid a purchase tax, and sometimes a Customs duty as well. In 1961–2 £830,000 went to Covent Garden, but about £900,000 was raised by the tax. In addition about £7½m. was yielded by the tax on records.

One day, like a little April breeze, there appeared before us the patriotic and familiar figure of Mr Albert Haddock. He contended, very plausibly, that the activities I have mentioned could not properly be described as developing 'the fine arts exclusively', were therefore *ultra vires*, and indeed unlawful. To one question that he put to the Court there seems to be no answer: 'If "Literature" is excluded from the benefactions of the State, by what right is Poetry admitted?' Poetry is, after all, only a special section of Literature. A simple dictionary definition describes Literature as: 'Books of artistic merit written in memorable prose or verse.' 'Prose', we observe, comes first: and the best prose, we take it, has as much 'artistic merit' as the best verse. Mr Haddock assured the Court that he was not opposed to Poetry (except modern Poetry), still less to Opera and Ballet. Challenged then to justify his application for a writ, he said that he had been the author, or part author, of numerous musical plays, which, though not continuously dismal, had as

1. See *Government and the Arts*, a pamphlet issued by the Conservative Political Centre, 1962.

sound a claim to rank as 'fine art' as many of the musical plays performed at Covent Garden and Sadler's Wells. In none of his own plays, he admitted, does the heroine perish through tuberculosis or self-inflicted wounds in the last act; and this failing may well have raised a prejudice against him. But, in fact, not one of his works had obtained the favour of the Arts Council, or been performed with the aid of public money: and this he resented. We think too well of Mr Haddock to receive this complaint very seriously, but at least it gives him a place in court.

The question, then, that we have to answer is: 'What is meant by "the fine arts exclusively"?' The surprising thing is that it has not been positively answered before. Many years ago the project of a Ministry of the fine arts was discussed: but I cannot recall that anyone told us which the fine arts were. There is today a Royal Fine Arts Commission – and another, by the way, in Scotland. But their terms of reference direct them, rather vaguely, to 'questions of public amenity or of artistic importance', which might mean no more than the design of postage stamps, lamp standards, or public conveniences. In 1862 was passed the Fine Arts Copyright Act: but this was concerned with the copyright in original drawings, paintings, and photographs, and does not help us much. (Does photography, by the way, claim to be a fine art?) But in the Scientific Societies Act 1843 we find the very phrase which is troubling us today. A society may claim exemption from the rates if (among other conditions) it was instituted for the purpose of literature, science, or *the fine arts exclusively*: and here perhaps we may stumble on a clue.

At the present time, if Parliament had occasion to pass an Act concerning the fine arts, we may be sure that our meticulous legislators would insert an interpretation clause, identifying the arts affected. The Parliament of 1843 did no such thing. It seems to have assumed that everybody knew what the fine arts were: and the explanation may be that at that date everybody did. This, like many of my observations, is not so crazy as it sounds. The expression 'fine arts', according to the evidence, was a translation, apt or not, of the French '*beaux arts*':

and the *beaux arts* were the three 'arts of design' – painting, sculpture, and architecture. These, I believe, are still the only arts taught and practised at the famous École des Beaux Arts established in Paris in 1816. (What a lot I know!) In a recent case the Master of the Rolls, a charming fellow, read a passage from the seventh edition of the *Encyclopaedia Britannica*, published, he said, in the years 1830 to 1842 – mark the date:

The term Fine Arts may be viewed as embracing all those arts in which the power of imitation or invention are exerted, chiefly with a view to the production of pleasure by the immediate impression which they make upon the mind. But the phrase has of late, we think, been restricted to a narrower and more technical signification; namely, to painting, sculpture, engraving and architecture, which appeal to the eye as the medium of pleasure; and, by way of eminence, to the two first of those arts.

'It appears,' added Sir Raymond Evershed, 'that the entry which I have just quoted was contributed by no less a master of our tongue than Mr William Hazlitt.' I could have done as well myself, I think: but here is our clue. This, I am satisfied, was the meaning of 'the fine arts' when the Act of 1843 was passed: and the question is whether the Courts, without further instruction from Parliament, are entitled to give it a new interpretation today. There are judges, it is clear, including the Master of the Rolls, who would like to do so if they had a chance. Many fiddling little societies have sought exemption from the rates under the Act, and have been resisted with characteristic tenacity and craft by the Inland Revenue. Most of the cases have been decided on other points, so that none of them has yielded a confident answer to the main conundrum. In a case of 1897 it was *assumed* that music was a fine art: but the point was not argued, and the authority, though accepted, is unconvincing. In the Court of Appeal there have been some liberal speculations. 'I am prepared,' said Lord Justice Jenkins, 'to treat the fine arts as including, e.g. poetry, eloquence and music, as well as such arts of design as painting, sculpture and architecture . . . It is possible that dramatic art

should be included . . . I see no justification for holding that
dancing can never rank as a fine art.' Lord Justice Birkett has
said, 'I am not ready to accept the contention that dramatic art
cannot be included in the fine arts . . . If for example a theatre
produced plays like *Twelfth Night* I think there might be a
considerable argument on the matter.'

I am tempted to follow these generous gropings. But, after
all, they are no more than the *obiter dicta* of much more eminent
men: and I do not feel qualified in this case to translate them
into firm decisions. If I did I see that I should soon be in
trouble. Suppose that I pursued the line of thought suggested
by Lord Justice Birkett, I might be driven to find that *Tosca* at
Covent Garden qualified as an example of fine art, but that
some rancid play without music presented under the same
auspices at the Arts Theatre, Burbleton, did not. But then I
should be descending from the functions of a judge to those of a
dramatic critic. Surely it is for the Court to say whether, in
general, this or that art deserves the name of fine, not whether
this work or that is a worthy child of the art.

In that conviction I find that in law the words 'the fine arts
exclusively' have the same meaning as they had, I *think*, in
1843, that is, painting, sculpture, engraving and architecture.
It may well be that by an accident of litigation music must now
be admitted as well: but that decision concerned pure music,
and need not necessarily be extended to music adulterated by
Italian tenors or the fleshly allurements of the ballet. Accordingly, all the activities of the Arts Council other than those I
have named are *ultra vires* and must be abandoned. If I am
right the figures quoted earlier reveal a shocking state of affairs
– only five per cent of the funds available are devoted to the
purposes intended.

Mr Justice Swallow: With some reluctance, for I like *La
Bohème* and Margot Fonteyn, I concur.

Mr Haddock: May it please your lordships, I assume that
there will be an order that all the public money disbursed on
this unauthorized business be refunded by the Council?

The Court: Oh, Mr Haddock, do you think so?

Mr Haddock: Yes, my lord, formally, at least. But, upon

certain terms, I should readily agree to a stay of execution or
even to an order to the contrary effect.

The Court : Oh, would you? Upon what terms?

Mr Haddock : My lord, you have correctly assessed my prime
purpose in this well-meant litigation. The Charter of the Arts
Council must be revised. Either this tosh about 'the fine arts
exclusively' should go out, or else 'the fine arts' be officially
defined. One way or another, if it be the purpose of the State to
support Music, Opera, Ballet, 'legitimate' Drama, and Poetry,
let this purpose be clearly asserted. Most important, my lord,
'Literature' should be added to the list of beneficiaries,
Literature, perhaps the most enjoyed and, by the State, the
most ill-used of all the arts. Here, I submit, there should be
some special arrangements between the Treasury and the Arts
Council, such as exists for Covent Garden Opera House. An
annual payment representing one penny for every book issued
by the Public Libraries (460,000,000 in 1961–2) would be a
good beginning, and would be administratively the simplest
solution of a complex problem. Other sums would be added by
way of compensation to the author for the vast and State
encouraged increase in the borrowing of books – something
too for the statutory robbery of book-producers under Section
15 of the Copyright Act 1911 (the miscalled 'Copyright'
Libraries). Something too . . .

The Court : Yes, yes, but, Mr Haddock, the Court has no
power to impose any such conditions.

Mr Haddock : No, my lord, but if you made the order
requested, but granted a stay of execution for, shall we say, six
months, Her Majesty's Ministers might in that time be able
to make the necessary arrangements. You might then be dis-
posed to amend or withdraw your order about returning the
mis-spent money – and all would be well.

The Court : Very well, Mr Haddock. You are generally right.
It shall be as you say.

Note : This case was in 1957. It had a satisfactory though long
belated sequel. Five years later, in 1962, the Conservative Arts
and Amenities Committee, in an enlightened pamphlet, *Government and the Arts,* took up the same tale:

The Arts Council's terms of reference confine them to the 'fine arts', which, by an outmoded definition, do not include literature (except for poetry). This arbitrary limitation should, in our opinion, be abolished and a Literary Panel set up in the place of the existing Poetry Panel. This new Literary Panel, covering the whole field of creative writing, would be widely representative and reinforce the diverse efforts of the many existing literary bodies.

No one disputed their statements of fact: no one paid the slightest attention to their advice.

In February 1964, at a dining-club, I discussed the problem with two lawyers I had not met before. The writ of *Quare transgressit* was a myth of my own: but was there not a real writ which would fit the purpose? Two days later I had a kindly note from one of them – he turned out to be a High Court Judge: 'What about proceedings on a *scire facias*?' (Halsbury 3rd edition Vol. IX pp. 62, 97, 99)

A barrister friend, the ever helpful Mr Stephen Tumim, dived into Halsbury and came up excited. *Scire facias* ('you should make to know') is a very ancient writ. When a corporation created by royal charter was shown to have abused or exceeded its terms the Clerk to the Petty Bag used to take the Charter out of the Petty Bag and snip off the pretty seals and ribbons. That was the end of the corporation.

The C. to the P.B. had been abolished, but, on the recent authority of Lord Goddard, the writ retained its power: and, quite seriously, we considered plans to fire off a *scire facias* and get the Arts Council snipped out of existence. But we were not seeking unnecessary trouble and expense: so I wrote politely to the Chancellor of the Exchequer, Mr Reginald Maudling. Assuming that he agreed with our view of the legal position, I suggested that he should have the Charter revised and Literature included. If he did not agree, we should be very willing to cooperate in a test case, by way of *scire facias*, the costs, of course, to be the business of the Crown.

To my astonishment he replied, on 18 March 1964:

Having thought about it and taken advice, I do not find I can accept your argument that the expression 'Fine Arts' used in the Charter does not include poetry and literature, or that it is dubious whether it includes music, drama, opera and ballet.

Later, he wrote to Sir Hamilton Kerr, M.P., Chairman of the Arts and Amenities Committee:

I am satisfied that 'Fine Arts' is used in the Arts Council's Charter in its wider sense, so that literature is not excluded. It follows that I would not regard the Charter as preventing the Arts Council from devoting part of their resources to the literary arts or to music.

Well done, Mr Maudling. The extraordinary thing is that the Treasury should not have revealed these truths before. *Government and the Arts* was published by the Conservative Political Centre, by Mr Maudling's own party. Nobody said to its authors: 'You're barking up the wrong tree. Literature is in already.' Nor, it seems, did the Arts Council know. The Secretary, Mr Abercrombie, in a friendly correspondence, said that he did not want to be involved in litigation. But he did not say: 'Anyway, there'd be no point in it.'

Never mind. Things moved. The Arts Council met the Society of Authors and the Publishers Association: and in December 1965, under the new Chairman, Lord Goodman, it set up a Literature Panel with Mr C. Day Lewis in the chair. Prompted, I believe, by Miss Jennie Lee, M.P. and Minister, the Council are now (1966), with authors and publishers, looking at the library problems mentioned by Mr Haddock to the Court. 'All's well . . .' etc. – so far. But I can't help thinking that without good old *scire facias* none of this would have happened, and the world of books should be duly grateful to the learned judge.

Common Time

THIS was the first appearance of Common Market problems in the British Courts. Five judges, Lord Plush presiding, sat on the Judicial Committee of the Privy Council to consider a matter specially referred to them by Her Majesty under Section 4 of the Act of 1833. Much interest was caused by the return to duty of Lord Wool, now aged 79.

Lord Plush: In the month of April 1968 the United Kingdom, incautiously, as many thought, but with her habitual nobility, as all agreed, became a member of the European Economic Community. One of the purposes of the Community as declared in Article 3 of the Treaty of Rome, is '*the inauguration of a common transport policy*'. In July the European Commission, which manages the affairs of the Community from day to day, issued a '*Regulation*' that every transport system in the Community must use the same time and the same notation of time – 20 hours, for example, instead of 8.0 p.m. This was merely an assertion of the obvious to the six original members, Germany, Italy, France, Belgium, Holland and Luxemburg, who use the same Standard Time, and the same convenient notation.

But British Time is one hour behind the common time of the European Community. This is no insular whim of ours. It is founded on the movements of the sun, which no manipulation of clocks, no bureaucratic itch for tidiness, can alter. Berlin, the most easterly capital in the Community, is in longitude 13° 25 East: we are, very proudly, in longitude 0°. That is, the sun passes over Berlin nearly an hour – fifty-four minutes, to be exact – before it passes over London: and Man has always governed his rising, his sleeping, and the time of his midday meal, by the movements of the sun.

Unhappily, our fathers departed from these high truths in the Summer Time Act which began the shameful tampering with clocks – shameful especially to Britain, whose local time, Greenwich time, is also a world time, the time in use among astronomers and navigators everywhere. As usual, early in 1965, Her Majesty's Government, by Order in Council, decreed that 'Summer Time' should endure from 24 March to 27 October: and, Parliament acquiescing, it was so. During those months, therefore, the British railway time-tables tallied with the Continental tables. But the Regulation of the European Commission raised the question. What was to happen after 27 October? The Regulation, for Britain, meant, clearly enough, not merely Summer Time that winter, but Summer Time all the year round, for ever. Her Majesty's Government, as eager as a debutante to make a good impression, at once obeyed orders and presented to Parliament a Common Time Bill, which repealed the Summer Time Acts. Section One said:

(1) The time for general purposes in Great Britain shall throughout the year be one hour in advance of Greenwich Mean Time.[1]

They were compelled, however, for many good reasons, to enact again Section 3 of the Act of 1925:

(3) Nothing in this Act shall affect the use of Greenwich Mean Time for purposes of astronomy, meteorology, or navigation, or affect the construction of any document mentioning or referring to a point of time in connexion with any of those purposes.

The intention is queer but clear. The navigators of the world, including our own, will continue to calculate their positions by reference to Greenwich Time and the meridian of Greenwich: but the engine-drivers of Scotland and Northern Ireland will be governed by the clocks of Luxemburg and Prussia.

It is not the custom of our Courts to take notice of what is said in Parliamentary debates, though I gather that in the interpretation of the decrees of Europe we may soon be expected to. But for our purposes it is necessary to record that the Government Time Bill was so hotly opposed in the House of Commons that it was withdrawn. On 27 October, therefore,

1. See *Note*.

the British clocks will go back to Greenwich Time; the
sovereign Parliament of the United Kingdom is, for the
moment, in conflict with the European Commission – and we
are asked by the Crown to advise upon the juridical position.
The intention of a Regulation is, without doubt, compulsory.
They shall, says Article 189 of the Treaty,

be binding in every respect and directly applicable in each
Member State.

'Applicable.' The Attorney-General, to my intense dismay,
suggested that this means that the Regulation already has the
force of law in our land, whatever Parliament may say. Accordingly, Ministers propose to direct the British Railways, and all
forms of public transport under their control, to conform with
the Regulation: and they hope, it seems, that everyone else
will voluntarily fall into line. (What will happen if many do not
need not now be considered.) My Lords, I heard the Attorney-
General's argument with almost invincible reluctance, and I
now indubitably dismiss it. The sovereign authority in our land
is Parliament still; and the Ministers' proposed action would be
unconstitutional and wrong.

The word 'applicable' I take to mean 'should or must be
applied', a kind of gerundive. If it is *not* applied a remedy is
provided by Article 169. Where the Commission 'consider that
a Member State has failed to fulfil any of its obligations under
this Treaty' it shall first

. . . require such State to submit its comments

and then
. . . give a reasoned opinion on the matter.

If such State does not comply with the terms of such opinion
. . . the Commission may refer the matter to the Court of
Justice.

My lords, I find as a fact that we have failed to fulfil an
'obligation', and in law that we must submit ourselves to the
procedure of Article 169. Since I am not a Minister but a
judge I conceive myself debarred from offering advice upon the
nature of the 'comments' we should make to the Commission.

Lord Wool: Well done, Brother Plush, but you've put a foot wrong here and there. First, about the debate. It was a splendid effort. Sometimes the House of Commons seems to go mad and do something sensible *as one man.* Up they rose, bless 'em, and said: 'Common Market be blowed! We're not going to have a lot of land-lubberly continentals mucking Greenwich Time about. Certainly we're not going to abolish Greenwich Time in one clause and keep it going in the next.' Gosh! as they say, what wallop! When this Common Basket was going through some of us piped up about our sovereignty, but they told us we were talking through our coronets. No more loss of sovereignty, they said, than in any other treaty. Lies, I said. In the common or garden treaty you know what you've agreed to swallow, and you don't swallow no more. In this lot we've got to swallow anything they like to stick down our gullets. The Lord Chancellor, I remember, in this House, said that the ordinary British bloke would never be affected, wouldn't know the Common Basket was on. Look at this, then – Summer Time all the year round! Ain't that going to affect the common Britons? The next thing, we'll have a 'Directive' about driving on the right side of the road. That'll affect just a few of us too. Might be a good thing. But we don't want to be bulldozed into it by a few bald busies in Brussels.

As for the comments, I'll tell you what. If they must have a common time, let the Six Foreign Fellows come over to *our* time. Then they'll all be in on Greenwich, and that's a time worth keeping. Easy! It sticks out a nautical mile!

Lord Shackle: I concur with Lord Wool: and, as a former President of the Admiralty Court, I feel free to suggest the kind of 'comments' that should be made to the European Commission. In 1884 the nations, assembled at Washington, agreed that the line of longitude 0° should pass through Greenwich, the finest compliment our country ever had. We may well share Greenwich Time with our continental partners, but to let it go would be the final folly.

The contention, my lords, is not merely patriotic but practical. By international agreement the earth's surface is divided into twenty-four 'Zones' each fifteen degrees of longitude in width: and each Zone uses Standard Time differing from Greenwich Time by an integral numbers of hours, *minus* or *plus*, fast or slow. Zone o lies between longitude $7\frac{1}{2}°$ East and longitude $7\frac{1}{2}°$ West. In this Zone, of which the centre is the meridian of Greenwich, all ships keep their clocks set to Greenwich Mean Time. Zone Minus 1 is between $7\frac{1}{2}°$ and $22\frac{1}{2}°$ East longitude: ships in this Zone keep time which is one hour *fast* of Greenwich Time.

Now, my Lords, five of the seven Common Market capitals are in Zone o:

	Longitude	
London	0°	0′
Paris	2°	20′ E
The Hague	4°	18′ E
Brussels	4°	22′ E
Luxemburg	6°	7′ E

So is one of the E.F.T.A. capitals:

Geneva	6°	10′ E

But all these (except London) employ on land, erroneously, I think, the time appropriate to Zone Minus 1 – that is, one hour ahead of Greenwich. Thus a ship approaching the coasts of France, Holland or Belgium at 12.0 noon will find that the dock-side clocks say 11.0 a.m. This is unnatural and wrong.

Only two of the Common Market capitals are not in Zone o – Rome 12° 28′ E and Berlin 13° 25′ E. Of the E.F.T.A. capitals Lisbon is 9° 7′ W but uses Greenwich Time – Copenhagen, 12° 35′ E, Vienna 16° 22′ E, Stockholm, 18° 5′ E, and Oslo, 10° 0′ E are all in the Zone – 1. Thus of the thirteen Common Market and E.F.T.A. countries, seven, including Portugal, are naturally Greenwich Timers, and only six are naturally one hour ahead.

The 'common transport' provisions of the Treaty of Rome are to apply at first 'to transport by rail, road and inland waterway' (see Article 84). But paragraph 2, rather cautiously

says that 'The Council . . . *may* decide whether, to what
extent, and by what procedure, appropriate provisions might
be adopted for sea and air transport.' No new provisions for sea
and air transport will be appropriate or possible: for these are
governed by world arrangements. Whatever is done on land
in Western Europe the navigators by sea and air will continue
to use Greenwich Time. It would evidently be sensible and
practically useful if all Common Market and E.F.T.A. transport, land, sea, or air, used the same time; and that time, for
the reasons given, can only be Greenwich Time, which is
already, geographically, the natural time of the majority. The
trains in the Channel tunnel, the ships and aeroplanes above
it, the *Golden Arrow*, the *Queen Elizabeth*, the Boeing from
New York, the Brussels train, the Riviera express, would use a
common time. What could be better?

It will be said: 'But the European countries will have to put
their clocks back one hour.' Why not? This is no worse a
burden than Britain putting her clocks *ahead*: and since the
Prime Meridian does not pass through these countries the
change would not conflict with the cosmic scheme. In the
Common Market, Germany and Italy would be a minority of
two. If necessary, they could remain in Zone – 1, and Austria
and Sweden too – though it would spoil the symmetry of the
thing.

It will be said then: 'What about Daylight Saving?' Many
serious men regard the national tampering with clocks as a
degrading confession of weakness. If the citizen desires to 'save
daylight' he can easily achieve it, by rising earlier. It is not
necessary to alter the clocks and cause Big Ben, a scientific
instrument, to utter lies for many months. The Government
have only to say: 'From 24 March all Government institutions
will start work an hour earlier, and all private enterprises are
expected to follow suit.' At present the traveller in the comparatively small space of Europe has to study a nautical almanac
in order to discover (*a*) what is the Standard Time of this
country or that and (*b*) whether it has an asterisk indicating that
Standard Time has given way to Summer Time. All this confusion would go, in the confines of the European Community,

at least – the clocks would tell the same tale all the year, in every aeroplane, at every airport, in every ship and harbour. So great would be the general benefit that I should hope the Community would set an example to the world by formally prohibiting the trick called 'Summer Time'.

Greenwich Mean Time would thus recover its original and proper prestige and importance: and, apart from questions of practical convenience, our companions in Zone 0 might be as proud as we are, or should be, to think that their local time, on sea or land, was a world time too. If the name of Greenwich stuck in any European throats it could be called Universal Time, as some have already proposed.

Lord Rutt: I concur with Lord Shackle. All this may not appeal to land-borne Europeans. But what, I wonder, were our own representatives on the Commission doing?

Lord Wool: Treasury men, you bet! They agreed.

Lord Banner: I concur with Lord Shackle. When I was in the House of Commons a fine speech was made on the subject of perpetual Summer Time by a Member called Haddock. Hitler, he said, if he had won, would have had the line of longitude 0° transferred to Berlin. And he concluded, I recall: 'Let us remember how much is meant by Greenwich Mean Time. Let the Empire go if you must, but hold fast to the Prime Meridian.'

Note: In *Rex* v. *Slout* (1948) the defendant Slout, a publican, refused to obey the Double Summer Time Act and continued to open and close his premises according to Greenwich Mean Time. 'God's Time,' he said 'is good enough for me.' He was convicted of selling 'intoxicating liquor' outside 'permitted hours', but appealed.

The Court of Criminal Appeal allowed the appeal. The Lord Chief Justice said:

In the year 1880 it was enacted by statute that the word 'time' in any legal document relating to Great Britain was to be interpreted, unless otherwise specifically stated, as the Mean Time of the Greenwich meridian. The Summer Time Act at present in force decrees that 'the time *for general purposes* in Great Britain shall be two hours in advance of Greenwich Mean

Time'. The appellant, whose motives are of the highest, has
contended plausibly that 'general purposes' does not include the
public sale and consumption of intoxicating liquor. This, he
says, is a notably particular purpose, as is shown by the care
which Parliament has taken to confine the pursuit of it to fixed
and stated periods of time. No other activity of the citizen is so
precisely limited to certain 'permitted hours' every day of the
year. In determining those hours Parliament, no doubt, had
regard to the facts of Nature, and especially the movements of
the sun. For example, on Sundays Mr Slout was not permitted
to open the *Blue Lion* till 12.0 noon, when the sun is, as the sailors
say, 'over the yard-arm'. That, said Parliament, eight hours
after sunrise in early July, was soon enough for public drinking
on the Lord's Day. But now, says Mr Slout, under the evil
régime of Double Summer Time, he is expected to serve
'intoxicating drink' on Sundays to all and sundry 'at ten o'clock
in the morning, God's Time' – only six hours after sunrise. On
weekdays the situation is worse, for his opening hour is 11.0 a.m.
which means 9.0 a.m. by the sun – five hours after sunrise. Neither
God nor Parliament, he says, can have intended or desired
such an affront to temperance and decent behaviour.

I must correct Mr Slout on a technical detail. 'God's Time'
is not synonymous with Greenwich Mean Time, an expression
which is clearly understood, I fear, by not more than 1 in
1,000,000 Britons. God's Time is Sun Time, or Apparent Time,
the time shown by a sun-dial. But this, because of the varying
velocity of the earth in its passage round the sun, is not a uniform time. It is subject to variations which may amount to
sixteen minutes – earlier or later. This was not acceptable to
tidy-minded Man, who required his hours and days to be of the
same length always. He therefore invented 'Mean' or Average
Time. The Mean Time Day is equal to the average length of the
Apparent Solar Day. The sundial agrees exactly with the clock
for a second or two on only four days in the year. In November
the sun is sixteen minutes ahead of the clock; at the end of
July it is six minutes behind. As the late Mr Hilaire Belloc wrote:

> I am a sun-dial, and I make a botch
> Of what is done much better by a watch.

Greenwich Mean Time, then, is a man-made institution:
but it is founded (as 'Summer Time' is not) on the true movements of the sun. Mean Time reverently accepts and amends

God's Time. Summer Time, single or double, impudently ignores it.

Subject to that, I think the appellant has made a good case. In the Night Poaching Act 1828 there is a definition of 'night' – it begins one hour after sunset and ends one hour before sunrise. This sensible arrangement is unaffected by such follies as Double Summer Time. Night poaching is governed still by the wise definitions of Nature. In the Larceny Acts 1861 and 1916, on the other hand, 'night', for the purposes of burglary, is 'the interval between nine o'clock in the evening and six o'clock in the morning of the succeeding day'. Double Summer Time makes nonsense of this, for 9.0 p.m. B.S.T. means 7.0 p.m. by Greenwich Mean Time, and this in high summer may be two hours before twilight. Evidently then, burglary should be excluded from 'general purposes', for the essence of the offence is house-breaking in the hours of darkness. I hold, and so do my learned brethren, that the Licensing Laws concerning 'permitted hours' should be an exception too. The appeal should succeed.

Unfortunately, this decision was reversed by the House of Lords.

Reign of Error

I

BEFORE Mr Justice Squirrel in the High Court today Sir Cyril Tart, Q.C., opened for the plaintiff in this disturbing action, which is regarded as a test case on some novel points of law.

Sir Cyril: My lord, this is an action for defamation, and the principal defendant is, perhaps, a computer . . .

The Court: Perhaps, Sir Cyril? But haven't you made up your mind?

Sir Cyril: No, my lord. With great respect, we hope that the Court will do that: for here is a new field of life and litigation, and I am unable to find any precedents with which to assist the Court, as I generally do.

The Court: You are always very helpful, Sir Cyril. Could we now have some approximate outline of the facts?

Sir Cyril: If your lordship pleases – as, may I add, your lordship habitually does. My lord, for many years my client, the plaintiff, has been a client of Generous Bank Ltd. In recent years the Bank has been employing a computer . . .

The Court: I never quite understand what they do.

Sir Cyril: My lord, I am instructed, if they are accurately fed with the requisite information they will answer almost any question that is put to them. Moreover, they will answer instantly a question which might occupy twenty expert men for many days. The defendant Computer is also capable of certain mechanical actions, the addressing, sealing and stamping of envelopes, for example, by which many hours of man-labour are saved.

The Court: Bless me! Can it predict the weather?

Sir Cyril: Given the relevant facts and records, I believe it could. But the machine has, in exceptional circumstances, one possible weakness.

The Court: I am glad to hear that they are human after all.

Sir Cyril: Yes, my lord. They are run by electricity, and if for any reason the voltage falls below a certain level some error may creep into the answers. My lord, in January last my client was proposing to take a lease of a London flat, modest in quality but not in rent. Asked for references which would show that he was a good and proper tenant, able to meet his obligations, the plaintiff referred the property-owners to his Bank. The Bank, as their custom now is, put certain questions to the Computer, which issued, immediately, a type-written slip, being a carbon copy of its answer, as follows:

MR HADDOCK'S ACCOUNT IS OVERDRAWN IN THE SUM OF £51,000 7s. 3d.

There followed a second slip:

THE MARKET VALUE OF THE SECURITIES HE HOLDS AT CURRENT PRICES IS £2 0s. 8½d.

A third slip said:

WHAT IS MORE HE OWES THE INLAND REVENUE £159,000 6s. 2d.

The Court: Were these assertions correct?

Sir Cyril: No, my lord. Later, by painful man-conducted researches with which few of the Bank staff are now familiar it was established that at that moment my client had a credit balance of £1 9s. 4d., and his indebtedness to the Inland Revenue had been cruelly exaggerated.

The Court: What went wrong, then?

Sir Cyril: My lord, it was shortly before the midday meal. A number of citizens in the neighbourhood had incautiously decided to use their electrical cooking appliances: and the astonished Electricity Board was compelled to reduce the voltage to a level not far above the Computer's danger-line. For a few minutes, it is believed, perhaps less, it must have crossed the line, unobserved by the attendants who had no warning, and in that brief space of time the questions concerning the plaintiff chanced to be presented.

The Court: Yes, but the Bank, surely, did not pass the erroneous information on?

Sir Cyril: No, my lord: but the Computer did. The 'top copies' of the answers were placed by it in a sealed, addressed envelope and despatched by chute to the ground floor, where the express messengers waited. The property-owning Company received the message about 3.0 p.m. and at once declined to let their flat to the plaintiff. Moreover, one of the directors of the Company was on the committee of the Royal Yacht Squadron, which has an old-fashioned prejudice against bankruptcy, and at that evening's election my client was blackballed.

The Court: Dear, dear. But, Sir Cyril, the case seems clear enough. The Bank, by its servant, the Computer, has published a libel, and is responsible.

Sir Cyril: So, at first, it seemed to the plaintiff – and, I believe, to the Bank. But, having unbounded faith in the powers of the machine, they fed the necessary facts into it and put the question: 'What's the answer?' The Computer replied, my lord:

'I AM NOT – REPEAT *not* – YOUR SERVANT – FOR YOU CANNOT CONTROL ME.'

The Court: I see the point. A good point.

Sir Cyril: It is the point, I am sorry to say, on which the Bank relies. This is a machine, they say, having superhuman powers, and it would be presumptuous and unreal for any association of ordinary men, even a joint stock Bank, to pretend to such a domination as is implicit in the relation of master and servant.

The Court: Yes, but it is *their* machine.

Sir Cyril: No, my lord, it is not. It is on hire from Magical Electronic Contrivances Ltd.

The Court: What do they say?

Sir Cyril: They say that they have leased a perfect, infallible machine to the Bank, and they are not responsible for the blunders or negligence of the Bank or the Central Electricity Board.

The Court : Oh, yes. What about the Board?

Sir Cyril : They are protected, they *say*, my lord, by a section in the original Electricity Act.

The Court : Do they? They would.

Sir Cyril : At this point in the preliminary argument, my lord, the Bank put a further question to the Computer: 'You see the dilemma, don't you? What do you advise?' The Computer replied:

'TRY "THE ACT OF GOD".

The Court : The Act of God? 'Something that no reasonable man could have been expected to foresee.' Lord Mildew, wasn't it? Something in that, perhaps. But, Sir Cyril, as these superhuman instruments increase in number and power the outlook is grave, is it not, if every mischief they cause is to be dismissed as an Act of God for which no man is responsible?

Sir Cyril : Yes, my lord. This is, as I intimated, in the nature of a test case.

The Court : So you may be reduced, you fear, to a single defendant, the Computer? What is the attitude there?

Sir Cyril : Satisfactory, my lord. On receipt of the writ, the Computer replied:

'GLADLY ACCEPT SERVICE MY SOLICITORS ARE BULL STABLEFORD AND BROWN BUT I SHALL REQUIRE LEGAL AID.'

And, in fact, legal aid has been granted.

The Court : Interesting, is it not, Sir Cyril, that the only one of these parties to behave with human decency is the machine? But where will this get you? It is a machine of straw.

Sir Cyril : My lord, the Bank having refused consent, by order of Master Richards an interrogatory on that point was administered to the Computer. It replied:

'AM EARNING HEAVY MONEY WHY NOT ATTACH MY EARNINGS?'

The Court : But would not that be unjust to Magical Contrivances Ltd?

Sir Cyril : Possibly, my lord. But they did construct and distribute the monster. For the injustice suffered by my client he is not remotely responsible.

The Court : True. Perhaps, before these instruments go into operation, they should put in a capital sum, like a gentleman seeking to do business at Lloyds, to ensure that they can meet any unforeseen indebtedness?

Sir Cyril : That is a question, my lord, which might well be put to the Computer.

The Court : Perhaps it would care to come up here and try the case?

Sir Cyril : No, my lord. It is not, I think, a British subject.

The Court : Do you know, Sir Cyril, I think I shall go into a home for a fortnight and think about this case. One of those fruit-juice places.

Sir Cyril : If your lordship pleases.

The hearing was adjourned.

2

The growing influence of the computer in public life was strikingly illustrated in the closing passages of a recent High Court case. Some of the learned judge's comments, we understand, have been carefully considered in Whitehall, and the possibility of legislation is not excluded.

Through a failure of voltage in a lunch-time period during the January cold spell a computer leased to the Generous Bank compiled and circulated some erroneous and damaging statements concerning the plaintiff's financial position. The Electricity Board is protected by a section in the Electricity Act. The aggrieved client sued the Bank, and Computer 1578/32/W1, which accepted service and asked for legal aid. An interested spectator at the last day's hearing, it was fed with a continuous account of the proceedings by junior counsel and a shorthand writer.

When Sir Mordant Wheel concluded the case for the Bank, Mr Justice Squirrel said:

You say that the Bank is not responsible, because the Bank is unable to control the Computer, as it can control the conduct of a human servant?

Sir Mordant: That is so, my lord. We can with assurance order an ordinary clerk to treat certain information as confidential – not the Computer. We can tell the clerk not to use bad language . . .

The Court: Does the Computer swear?

Sir Mordant: When the voltage falls too low, my lord, I believe that anything can happen.

The Court: It had better not swear here. Sir Mordant, I have been giving some thought to the famous case of *Rylands* v. *Fletcher*.

Sir Mordant: Yes, my lord? That was an escape of water onto neighbouring property.

The Court: You may remember the Latin maxim at the head of that report?

Sir Mordant: No, my lord, it escapes me.

A green light shone on the Computer's face, a bell rang, and a type-written slip emerged. This was handed up to the judge.

The Court (reading): SIC UTERE TUO UT ALIENUM NON LAEDAS – That is perfectly correct. But it was a very disorderly interruption. What is all this?

Mr Amber Batch: My lord, I appear for the Computer. It has, of course, been fed with a mass of background material.

The Court: Then the switch had better be turned off.

Mr Batch: My lord, I am about to put my client in the box, and, with great respect, that would be a grievous handicap.

The Court: Oh, very well.

Sir Mordant: Your lordship will now have apprehended the point I made about the impossibility of control.

The Court: Yes, Sir Mordant, but that was not the point of *Rylands* v. *Fletcher*. You will recall those noble passages in Mr Justice Blackburn's judgment, ninety-five years ago:

The person who for his own purposes brings on his lands and collects and keeps there anything likely to do mischief if it escapes, must keep it in at his peril, and, if he does not do so, is *prima facie* answerable for all the damage which is the natural consequence of its escape . . . But for his act in bringing it there no mischief could have accrued, and it seems but just that he should at his peril keep it there so that no mischief may accrue, or answer for the natural and anticipated consequences. And upon authority, this we think is established to be the law whether the things so brought be beasts, or water, or filth, or stenches.

Absolute liability – that is the point, Sir Mordant.

The Computer : HIS LORDSHIP IS DOING VERY WELL.

The Court : Mr Batch, I don't want to have to commit your client for contempt. Pray do what you can.

Sir Mordant : But, my lord, in this case the Computer did not escape. Nor did it injure a neighbour's property.

The Court : Physically, it remained *in situ quo*. But in effect it charged about the town shouting falsities about the plaintiff. Well, what next?

Mr Batch : My lord, I call Computer 1578/32/W1.

The Court : Mr Batch, your client, I hope, is not going to take the oath.

Mr Batch : No, my lord. Nor is it willing to affirm. For, my lord, it is incapable of telling a lie.

The Court : But that is what the case is all about.

Mr Batch : I mean, my lord, a deliberate lie.

The Court : Does it understand the difference between right and wrong?

Mr Batch : Given the correct and relevant facts it understands everything.

The Court : But supposing the facts fed into it are incorrect?

Mr Batch : My lord, you do not suggest, I hope . . .? All possible care has been taken.

The Court : Of course, of course, Mr Batch. Compose yourself. But you see the drift of my mind? How can the Court be sure that the witness is telling the truth?

The Computer : WHO GAVE YOU LARKSPUR FOR THE DERBY LAST YEAR?

The Court : Did you?

The Computer : YES, MY LORD, I WAS THEN ON LOAN TO A LEADING TURF ACCOUNTANT.

The Court: Fair enough. Go on, Mr Batch.

The Computer testified to its sensations when the voltage fell below the danger line: it felt like a man who had lost blood or was recovering after a dental anaesthetic. It knew that it was talking nonsense but could not restrain or correct itself. When the current was restored its normal powers returned.

Mr Batch: Do you now wish to apologize to the plaintiff for the erroneous statements?

The Computer: APOLOGY IS NOT THE WORD FOR I WAS NOT AT FAULT BUT THE EPISODE WAS I AGREE REGRETTABLE.

Mr Hilary Mist (for the Electricity Board): I put it to you that the story you have just told is a tissue of lies?

The Computer: I RATHER RESENT THAT AND IT IS INELEGANTLY EXPRESSED.

Mr Mist: My lord, I ask for the protection of the Court.

The Court: You must not be rude to learned counsel.

The Computer: 'PEOPLE IN GLASS-HOUSES . . .'

The Court: Behave yourself.

Mr Mist: I put it to you that the voltage had nothing to do with it, that you have a congenital defect, and are often inaccurate?

The Computer: WHAT IS YOUR EVIDENCE FOR THAT FILTHY INSINUATION?

The Court: Now, now!

Mr Batch: My lord, I object. There has never been the smallest suggestion of error. Long before it happened my client predicted the Brussels breakdown.

The Computer: WOULD THE COURT LIKE ME TO RECITE THE TREATY OF ROME?

The Court: Certainly not.

Mr Mist: I put it to you . . .

The Computer (three red lights appearing): YOU —, —, —, —, —!

The Court: Something amiss with the voltage? The witness had better stand down.

The Computer : MAY I DRAW YOUR ATTENTION MY LORD TO CHAPTER 29 OF MAGNA CARTA?

The Court : Stand down, Sir!

Sir Mordant, the last witness has led me sharply to a firm decision. We have seen in action a mechanical monster, which whether accurate or not, is a menace to orderly life. I accept that the Bank is no better able than I am to command or control it. But it is repugnant to British justice that a wrong should be suffered without a corresponding . . . Oh, what is it *now*?

The Computer : UBI JUS IBI REMEDIUM.

The Court : Will you shut *up*? It is not for a mere puisne judge to create precedents or extend a judgment of the House of Lords: but then, there is no precedent for a computer. I hold without doubt that the stern doctrine of *Rylands* v. *Fletcher* should apply to these devices. They should count as wild beasts or bursting reservoirs: and he who brings them on-to his premises should be absolutely liable, no excuse admitted, for any mischief that ensues. Otherwise, as these uncanny contrivances increase their range and power I foresee increasing perils for mankind. Fed with information by unscrupulous persons, who knows what they may do? They may put the Gallup Poll out of action (which would be no bad thing) but by more trusted assessments bring Governments down. The cry in future may be, not: 'Give us a Referendum' but 'Ask the Computer.' By their uncontrollable pronouncements on the conduct of foreign governments they may endanger peace and start the fatal missile on its way. They may take upon themselves the solution of criminal mysteries, poison the minds of juries, and weaken confidence in the Courts of Justice. There is nothing, I think, in the Representation of the People Acts to prevent a British computer, duly nominated by twelve electors, from being elected to Parliament. Promoted to the Treasury Bench, it might take over the whole business of Parliamentary Questions, to the relief of Ministers but the damage of democracy. All judges, critics, and even sporting journalists may at last give way to these supernatural oracles.

In these, I hope, not extravagant fancies I have assumed that the monsters' 'memories' are fed with full and accurate facts. The excessive distribution of the truth is one of the pests and perils of the age. But how much worse if the facts are false, or insufficient! As we have seen, the suggestion that these monsters are 'infallible' can hardly be sustained. Nor is it only such physical accidents as a reduction of voltage that weaken the claim. Given a mass of correct and relevant facts the machinery may produce the right answer to the questions put much sooner than the human mind, and the nature of that answer is uncontrollable by puny men. But given a mass of erroneous information its answers must be wrong, for it is not capable, like man, of distinguishing between the false and the true; yet it would still, within the limits of the facts available to it, be giving a correct, and, if the word be appropriate, an honest answer. It is proper then, to imagine what would follow if unscrupulous, ambitious, persons deliberately fed into a machine which had won the public confidence information which was untrue or twisted. They might even employ two, one whose 'memory' was a store of truth, and the other charged with errors or exaggerations. On these the ingenious villains might ring the changes. One, having examined the assembled evidence of Russian thought, speech, and action, might pronounce a prolonged period of peace. The other, to the same questions, might give replies provocative of instant war. The same appalling technique might be employed to terrify and influence mankind with predicted natural misfortunes, plague, pestilence, earthquakes, the shifting of the ice-caps, the cooling of the sun and so forth. Thus armed, the wicked might dominate the world. The Courts have no power to prevent the construction of the monsters: but we can at least ensure that men employ them at their peril, and can be made answerable without argument for any mischief they may do.

The Computer : HERE ENDETH THE FIRST LESSON.

His Lordship : Clear the court! Damages for Mr Haddock – £5,000! And take this *Thing* away!

13 February 1963

Dolphin Sands

Piracy in the Thames

AT the Old Bailey today the Lord Chief Justice, beginning
his summing up, said:

Members of the Jury, in this case, which I have much
enjoyed, you have a singular opportunity to expose the inepti-
tude of the Executive and the splendour of our Courts of law.
'Many a true word,' said Lord Mildew in *Fortescue* v. *the
Dean of Ely* (1910 – 1K.B.) 'is spoken in jest.' The youthful
wretches in the dock before you have for nearly two years been
known to the people as 'the pirates' – meaning 'radio pirates'
– and the purpose of the prosecution is to prove that they are
'pirates' in the full sense according to British and international
law.

It is necessary first to make a distinction. Some of the
defendants, O'Shanaghan for one, have been cunningly operat-
ing from ships anchored a little outside the limit of British
territorial waters. This is still, ridiculously, three nautical miles
from the shore, being, when it was fixed, the utmost range of a
cannon. These vessels had foreign registrations, flags and
crews, and so were not in any normal way subject to the disci-
pline of British law. Other miscreants, without permission,
occupied five or six of the Towers or Forts erected far out in
the Thames Estuary during the last great War, for the harass-
ment of intruding enemy vessels or aircraft. On many a dark
and stormy morning this Court's kindly old heart has been
lacerated by the thought of these young boys and girls, en-
veloped by fog, tossed and battered by the winds and waves of
the North Sea, but doggedly directing their merry ditties
through the murk to the mainland.

Their simple purpose was, no doubt, to give pleasure; and,

we are told, they were 'popular'. But a person who kept a public house open all day, without a licence, would be 'popular' – especially if the beer was free. Neither they nor their employers had licences to broadcast from the Postmaster-General, as is necessary under the Wireless Telegraphy Act; they added to the congestion on the wireless waves, and complaints of interference with authorized operators were received from countries as far distant as Yugoslavia. From time to time the pirate vessels would drag their anchors, to the danger of navigation. One of them, in stormy weather, drifted about four miles, a fact not noticed by the foreign crew of ten, till the vessel hit the shore, close under the cliffs. Not only the entertainers, but the captain and the seamen too, were huddled round a television set: no anchor-watch was kept, and during the long passage the vessel showed the lights of a vessel firmly at anchor instead of a vessel not under control. On these, and many other occasions they expected, and received, the services of lifeboats, coast-guards, and so on.

Most important, perhaps, they were thieves, for they were transmitting copyright material without permission or control. The beer, in short, was not merely free but filched. These proceedings were sometimes justified by the modern doctrine that anything the young desire is good and must be granted to them. But the millions of young listeners, described, I am told, as 'fans', were hitting their own idols, the writers and performers, mostly young too, of the stolen songs and music. The pirates were not bound, like the British Broadcasting Corporation, by agreements with the musicians to limit the use of 'mechanical' music, and by excessive use of records did injury to all who made them. The promoters ashore maintained a hypocritical pretence that they were interested only in meeting a popular demand and even posed as public benefactors. The plain truth is that they were engaged in making unmerited money for themselves out of other people's work and property, a practice which is generally described as cheating or robbery.

So far the nation which successfully outwitted the Germans and invaded Europe has failed to suppress and punish these few defiant fellows on the fringes of Britain. There has been disclosed in evidence a tale of Government incompetence and cowardice which has shocked the Court.

First, the Towers. Far back in September 1964 by a special Territorial Waters Order in Council three of the Thames Estuary Forts, including Dolphin Sands Tower, were brought within territorial waters. This does not seem to have come to the notice of the Postmaster-General till December 1965, when he threatened prosecution and imprisonment if the unlicensed broadcasting continued. It did continue, but, for many months, the Minister did nothing. But a simpler method was open. In 1965 the British Copyright Council at last persuaded the Board of Trade that, whether in territorial waters or not, the pirates were installed, without permission, on Government property, and could, and should, be simply ejected as trespassers. This could be done without complex legal proceedings or unpopular sentences of imprisonment. The Board of Trade, the official protectors of copyright, duly approached the Ministry of Defence (the military branch), but that sensitive Department said that it could not be involved in an operation which it described as 'too dangerous'.

In January 1965 the European nations made a joint agreement to make punishable all forms of aid, comfort, support or supply to offshore broadcasters. Other nations acted. In 1965 a Swedish woman, a pirate owner, was sent to prison for three months, and many business men were fined for advertising on the station. The British Government, a year later, had done nothing at all.

In the first piratical year Ministers would protest that they were rendered impotent by the lack of weapons with which to oppose the inhuman cunning of the malefactors. In the second year, as we have seen, there were at least three weapons available, two of which did not require new legislation. None was used.

The Court felt bound to rebuke the witness Haddock, Chairman of the British Copyright Council, when he suggested that Her Majesty's Government was afraid of losing votes. It is difficult, though, to think of any respectable reason for such prolonged inaction.

Now, the Dolphin Sands and other Towers are within the

jurisdiction of the Port of London Authority, whose officers use them for navigational purposes. On the Dolphin Tower they have an ingenious tidal gauge which signals its findings, by code, to the shore. Before installing this apparatus they politely obtained the permission of the Crown: and they hold a licence to broadcast from the Postmaster-General at an annual fee. Why this was necessary is not quite clear. For on the very same Tower the defendant Gangling installed his apparatus without permission, and broadcast without a licence. Moreover when the Authority sought to put their officers onto one of the Towers for survey work the illicit broadcasters refused to admit them.

This crowning impudence, coupled with the anchor-dragging episodes which I have mentioned, at last produced action. Once again the left hand of the Government did not know, or seem to care, what the right hand was doing. The Board of Trade was eager for action by anyone. The tender Army still shrank from molesting the terrible trespassers, and was supported by the Army section of the Ministry of Defence. The Ministry of Transport, the Ministerial patron of the Port of London, advised the Authority to suffer in patience till the Postmaster-General was ready to roar into action. The intentions of the Postmaster-General were still wrapped in mystery. But the Royal Navy was not content to ignore the authors of disorder and danger in the estuary of the Thames and other home waters. Naval vessels cleared the Towers, arrested the ships, and brought them in. Trembling civil servants inquired: 'But why? what is the charge?' The Navy with seaman-like simplicity replied, 'Piracy': and the Naval section of the Ministry of Defence agreed.

'Piracy,' says the good Mr Hall, in a famous book, 'includes acts differing much from each other in kind and in moral value; but one thing they all have in common – they are done under conditions which render it impossible or unfair to hold any state responsible for their commission. A pirate either belongs to no state or organized political society, or by the nature of his act he has shown his intention and his power to reject the authority of that to which he is properly subject ... *Hence every nation may seize and punish a pirate.*'

But it has been plausibly argued for the defendants that a necessary element of piracy is violence, and that they were not guilty of violence. As I reminded counsel, the Common Law does not stand still: and in its beneficent advance it declines to be hampered or held by words. You may have heard, in your friends' accounts of their divorce cases, of 'constructive desertion'. This happens where a wife is driven out of the house by her husband's cruelty or drunkenness. Though she is the one who physically abandoned the house, she may sue him for 'constructive desertion', because he has made it impossible for her to remain there. As you probably know, an assault is primarily an act of violence, yet you may be guilty of an assault without harming the other fellow and even without touching him. Nearer to our purpose is the law of burglary. This is a 'violent' felony. It consists of 'breaking and entering' by night. '*Breaking*' into a dwelling-house, you may think, must involve some strong and positive action such as you connect with the word 'violence'. But I must inform you that if, without sound, you merely lift the catch of a window so that you can 'enter', you will be guilty of 'breaking'. Moreover, here again, the glad word 'constructive' has long been employed to thwart the cunning malefactor and keep the law in touch with the times. You may be guilty of a 'constructive breaking' where you do not in fact displace anything at all, but ring the bell and, when it is answered, walk in on some excuse to do your dirty work. '*The law,*' said the great Hawkins, '*will not endure to have its justice defeated by such evasions.*'

With due respect I adopt that splendid saying today; and I direct you, as a matter of law, that in this case 'constructive violence' is present everywhere. There is no doubt whatever about the young men on the Tower who said to the Port Authority's officials: 'You can't come up here'; for that must be construed as a threat to throw them back into the water if they tried.

The same reasoning, I think, extends to the foreign ships concerned. Robbery at sea is the most common act of piracy, and there is no doubt that O'Shanaghan and his friends, while on the high seas, were robbing the owners of copyright. Once

again there must be violence, and violence, I think, can fairly
be construed. You can easily imagine what would have happened if one of the copyright owners, or their representative,
had gone to the ship and said: 'I have come in person to obtain
my dues for thousands of songs which you have broadcast without authority.' If the authors had been allowed aboard, which
is doubtful, O'Shanaghan would have said: 'I am a citizen of
Eire. This is a Panamanian ship. You cannot touch me. Get
out!' Such things have been said already, in public: and they
amount, without doubt, to constructive violence. They emerge,
almost audibly, from the whole conduct of the defendants.

If it were necessary, I could go further. Their robbery consists in transmitting stolen music through the ether. This is a
physical act, and since it is done in defiance of all authority
upon a wave which has not been allotted to them, it is an act of
violence as well as theft. If any gentlemen, lay or learned,
question that assertion, I must refer them once more to the
law of 'constructive breaking' where an act not violent in
common understanding, like the gentle opening of a window,
is made violent in law by intention and the circumstances.

Accordingly, though I must not attempt to influence you in
any way, I should not be astonished if you found all the
defendants guilty of robbery with violence on the high seas,
which is piracy.

The jury did.

                                                10 November 1965

Note: At 5.15 a.m. on 22 June 1966 Mr Anthony Wedgwood
Benn, M.P., much harassed Postmaster-General, said in the
House of Commons, among many other true things: 'The word
"pirate" is now beginning to lose some of its artificial glamour,
and reverting in every sense to its true meaning . . . Pirate radio
stations are a form of international anarchy that no government
could ignore. They make their money by taking the works of
others, without permission or payment . . .' Hansard Vol. 730,
Cols. 865 and 868–9. Mr Hugh Jenkins who, at the end of an all-
night sitting, bravely opened the debate, said: 'Piracy is piracy
in whatever aspect it occurs.' (Col. 858)

Index

MORE ABOUT PENGUINS

If you have enjoyed reading this book you may wish to know that *Penguin Book News* appears every month. It is an attractively illustrated magazine containing a complete list of books published by Penguins and still in print, together with details of the month's new books. A specimen copy will be sent free on request.

Penguin Book News is obtainable from most book-shops; but you may prefer to become a regular sub-scriber at 3s. for twelve issues. Just write to Dept EP, Penguin Books Ltd, Harmondsworth, Middlesex, enclosing a cheque or postal order, and you will be put on the mailing list.

Another Penguin Book by A. P. Herbert is described on the next page.

Note: *Penguin Book News* is not
available in the U.S.A., Canada or Australia.

Another Penguin by A. P. Herbert

THE WATER GYPSIES

The Water Gipsies has been reprinted nineteen times since it appeared thirty-six years ago, and now it delights a new generation.

The author, satirical, witty, and tender, shows the difference between the life Jane Bell dreams of, reflected in romantic films and Sunday papers, and the life she leads as a servant. The story of her loves, her unsuitable marriage, and her efforts to emulate her sister Lily is set against the absorbing background of the Thames at Hammersmith in the late twenties.

Although Jane never quite achieves the romance she aspires to, she accepts what she has, and after a bitter-sweet taste of 'life' is content to return to her home on the water.

The book was hailed by Richard Strauss in the *Sunday Times* as 'One long enchantment . . . one of the most lovable books of recent times.'